Table of Contents

How to Use This Book

This Premium Education Series workbook is designed to suit your teaching needs. Since every child learns at his or her own pace, this workbook can be used individually or as part of small group instruction. The activity pages can be used together with other educational materials and are easily applied to a variety of teaching approaches.

Contents
A detailed table of contents lists all the skills that are covered in the workbook.

Units
The workbook is divided into units of related skills. Numbered tabs allow you to quickly locate each unit. The skills within each unit are designed to be progressively more challenging.

Activity Pages
Each activity page is titled with the skill being practiced or reinforced. The activities and units in this workbook can be used in sequential order, or they can be used to accommodate and supplement any educational curriculum. In addition, the activity pages include simple instructions to encourage independent study, and they are printed in black and white so they can be easily reproduced. Plus, you can record the child's name and the date the activity was completed on each page to keep track of learning progress.

Practice Test
A comprehensive practice test helps prepare the child for standardized testing in a stress-free environment. Presented in the fill-in-the-circle format, this test includes skills covered on standardized tests.

Answer Key
The pages in the back of the workbook provide answers for each activity page as well as the practice test. These answer pages allow you to quickly check the child's work and provide immediate feedback on how he or she is progressing.

Name_____ Date_____

Color to show the number.

| 9 |
| 7 |
| 5 |
| 10 |
| 6 |
| 8 |

Name_____ Date_____

Count. Write how many.

1.

   3 + 3 = 6

2.

   4 + 1 = _____

3.

   2 + 5 = _____

4.

   5 + 4 = _____

5.

   3
   + 1
   _____

6.

   6
   + 2
   _____

7.

   4
   + 6
   _____

Name_____ Date_____

Write how many.

1.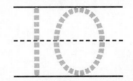

+ _____

_____ in all

2.

+ _____

_____ in all

3.

+ _____

_____ in all

4.

+ _____

_____ in all

5.

+ _____

_____ in all

6.

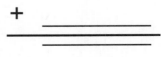

+ _____

_____ in all

Name_____ Date_____

Circle the correct number sentence.

1.  $3 + 7 = 10$

    $3 \quad\quad + \quad\quad 6$ $\boxed{3 + 6 = 9}$

2.     $5 + 4 = 9$

    $5 + 5 = 10$

3.     $7 + 3 = 10$

    $8 + 2 = 10$

4.     $6 + 3 = 9$

    $6 + 2 = 8$

5.    $0 + 7 = 7$

    $6 + 1 = 7$

6.  $3 + 6 = 9$

    $3 + 5 = 8$

Name_____ Date_____

Add to find the sums.

1.

$$\begin{array}{r} 7 \\ + 3 \\ \hline \end{array}$$
$$\begin{array}{r} 5 \\ + 4 \\ \hline \end{array}$$
$$\begin{array}{r} 2 \\ + 2 \\ \hline \end{array}$$
$$\begin{array}{r} 2 \\ + 7 \\ \hline \end{array}$$

2.

$$\begin{array}{r} 0 \\ + 9 \\ \hline \end{array}$$
$$\begin{array}{r} 5 \\ + 2 \\ \hline \end{array}$$
$$\begin{array}{r} 3 \\ + 6 \\ \hline \end{array}$$
$$\begin{array}{r} 1 \\ + 2 \\ \hline \end{array}$$

3.

$$\begin{array}{r} 2 \\ + 8 \\ \hline \end{array}$$
$$\begin{array}{r} 3 \\ + 5 \\ \hline \end{array}$$
$$\begin{array}{r} 6 \\ + 1 \\ \hline \end{array}$$
$$\begin{array}{r} 2 \\ + 3 \\ \hline \end{array}$$

Addition Facts to 10 (II)

Name____ Date____________________

Find the sums. Then use the code to color the picture.

10 = red
9 = blue
8 = green
7 = yellow
6 = orange

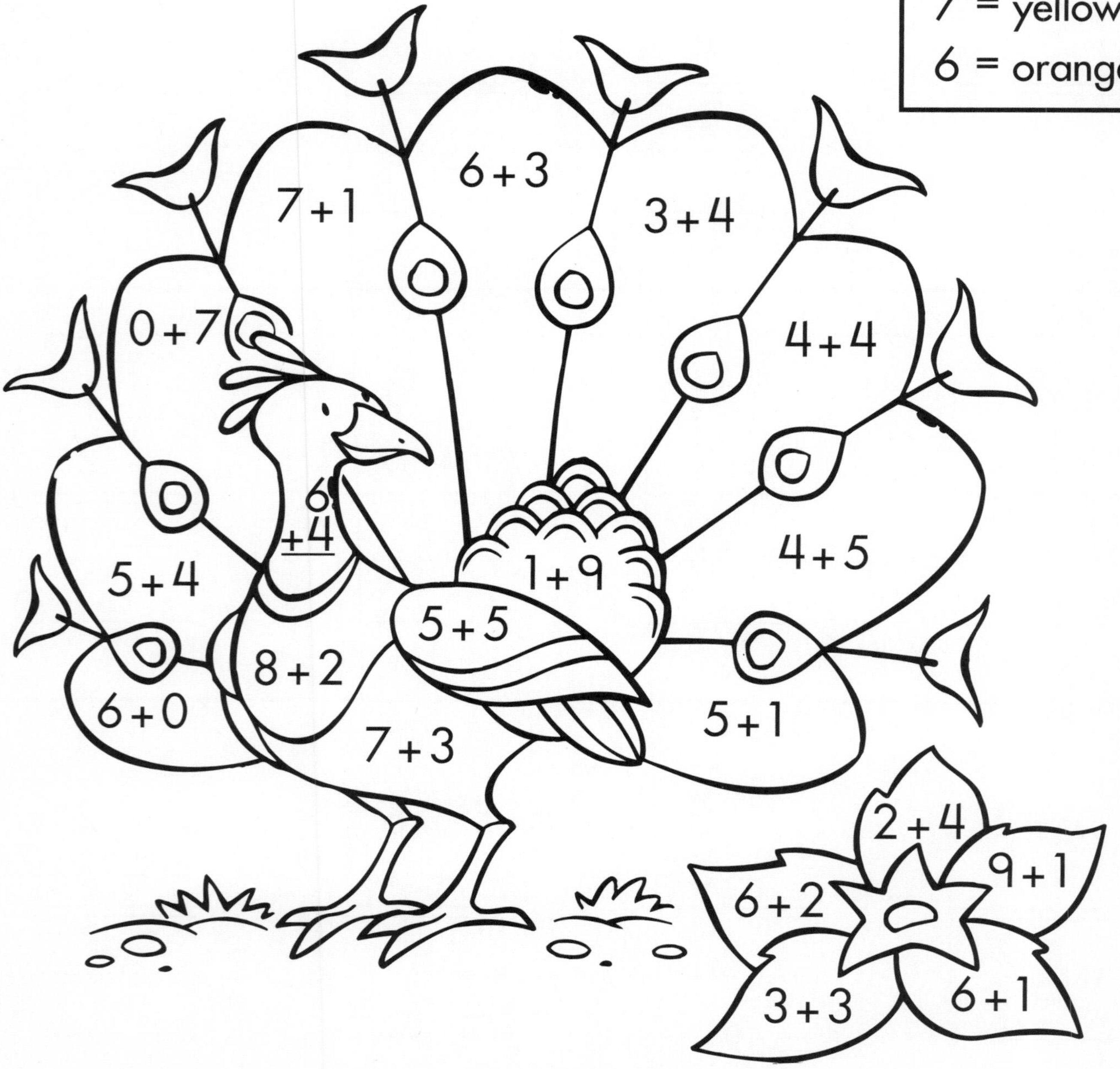

6 + 3
7 + 1
3 + 4
0 + 7
4 + 4
6
+4
4 + 5
5 + 4
1 + 9
5 + 5
8 + 2
6 + 0
7 + 3
5 + 1
2 + 4
9 + 1
6 + 2
3 + 3
6 + 1

Addition Facts to 10 (III)

Name________________________ Date______________

Unit 1

Add.

1. $5 + 5 =$ ______ $3 + 3 =$ ______

2. $8 + 1 =$ ______ $2 + 7 =$ ______

3. $3 + 2 =$ ______ $3 + 0 =$ ______

4. $6 + 3 =$ ______ $4 + 4 =$ ______

5. $2 + 1 =$ ______ $6 + 4 =$ ______

6. $5 + 2 =$ ______ $1 + 4 =$ ______

7. $7 + 3 =$ ______ $6 + 0 =$ ______

Addition Facts to 10 (IV)

Name_____ Date_____

Add.

1.
$$\begin{array}{r} 4 \\ +6 \\ \hline \end{array}$$
$$\begin{array}{r} 3 \\ +3 \\ \hline \end{array}$$
$$\begin{array}{r} 6 \\ +2 \\ \hline \end{array}$$
$$\begin{array}{r} 9 \\ +1 \\ \hline \end{array}$$
$$\begin{array}{r} 7 \\ +0 \\ \hline \end{array}$$

2.
$$\begin{array}{r} 8 \\ +1 \\ \hline \end{array}$$
$$\begin{array}{r} 2 \\ +1 \\ \hline \end{array}$$
$$\begin{array}{r} 3 \\ +6 \\ \hline \end{array}$$
$$\begin{array}{r} 4 \\ +3 \\ \hline \end{array}$$
$$\begin{array}{r} 1 \\ +4 \\ \hline \end{array}$$

3.
$$\begin{array}{r} 5 \\ +5 \\ \hline \end{array}$$
$$\begin{array}{r} 2 \\ +3 \\ \hline \end{array}$$
$$\begin{array}{r} 4 \\ +4 \\ \hline \end{array}$$
$$\begin{array}{r} 3 \\ +1 \\ \hline \end{array}$$
$$\begin{array}{r} 6 \\ +2 \\ \hline \end{array}$$

4.
$$\begin{array}{r} 2 \\ +8 \\ \hline \end{array}$$
$$\begin{array}{r} 3 \\ +5 \\ \hline \end{array}$$
$$\begin{array}{r} 6 \\ +0 \\ \hline \end{array}$$
$$\begin{array}{r} 4 \\ +5 \\ \hline \end{array}$$
$$\begin{array}{r} 4 \\ +1 \\ \hline \end{array}$$

Turnaround Addition Facts

Name_____ Date_____

$$4$$
$$+\,3$$
$$\overline{7}$$

The sum is the same. ←→

$$3$$
$$+\,4$$
$$\overline{7}$$

Write the sums. Then match.

1.
$$5$$
$$+\,4$$
$$\overline{9}$$

$$2$$
$$+\,6$$

5.
$$3$$
$$+\,2$$

$$2$$
$$+\,3$$

2.
$$3$$
$$+\,7$$

$$4$$
$$+\,5$$
$$\overline{9}$$

6.
$$3$$
$$+\,6$$

$$4$$
$$+\,6$$

3.
$$6$$
$$+\,2$$

$$7$$
$$+\,0$$

7.
$$5$$
$$+\,2$$

$$6$$
$$+\,3$$

4.
$$0$$
$$+\,7$$

$$7$$
$$+\,3$$

8.
$$6$$
$$+\,4$$

$$2$$
$$+\,5$$

Name_____ Date_____

Count how many are left. Write the number.

1.

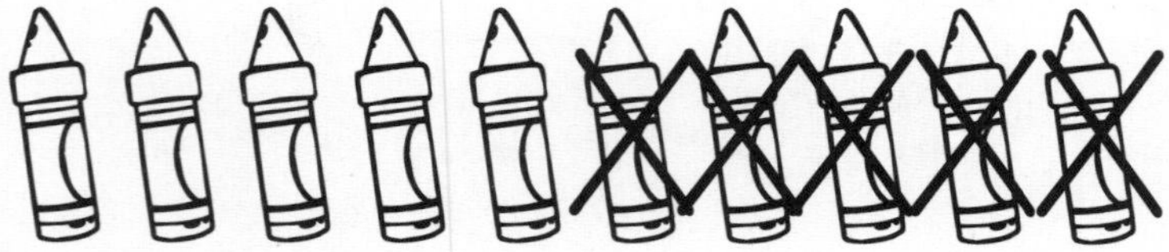

How many are left? $10 - 5 =$ _____ 5

2.

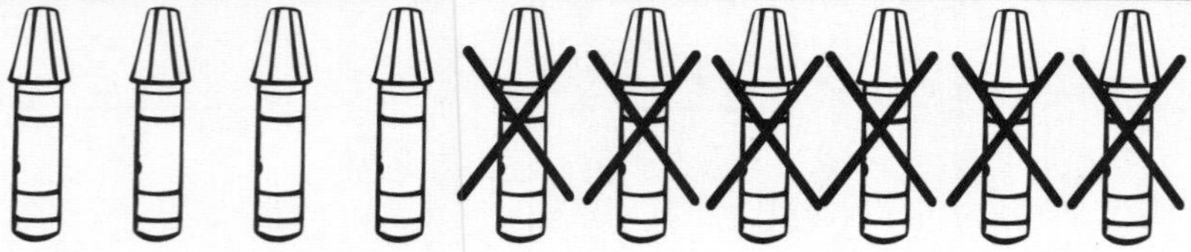

How many are left? $10 - 6 =$ _____

3.

How many are left? $9 - 5 =$ _____

4.

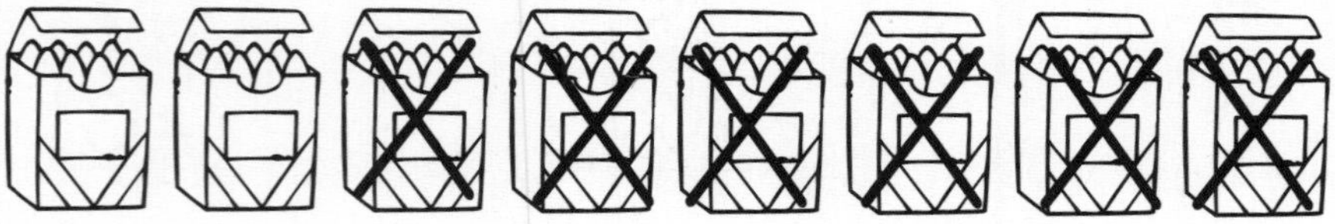

How many are left? $8 - 6 =$ _____

5.

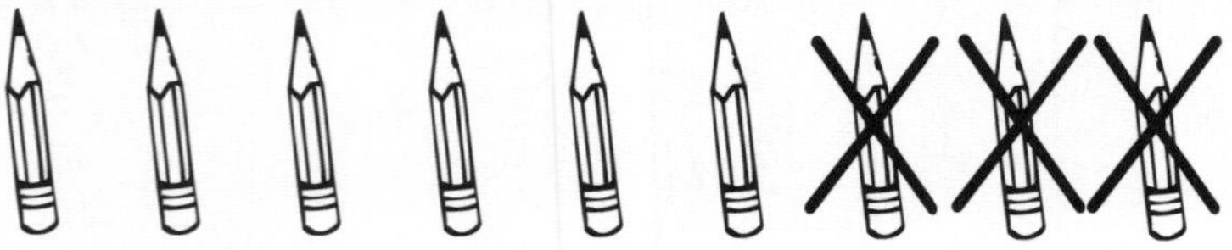

How many are left? $9 - 3 =$ _____

Subtraction: Sets (II)

Name_____ Date_____

Cross out and subtract.

1.

$$\begin{array}{r} 9 \\ -\ 4 \\ \hline \end{array}$$

5

2.

$$\begin{array}{r} 9 \\ -\ 8 \\ \hline \end{array}$$

- - - - - - - - -

How many are left? _____

3.

$$\begin{array}{r} 10 \\ -\ 8 \\ \hline \end{array}$$

- - - - - - - - -

How many are left? _____

4.

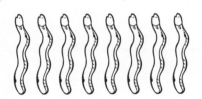

$$\begin{array}{r} 8 \\ -\ 5 \\ \hline \end{array}$$

- - - - - - - - -

How many are left? _____

5.

$$\begin{array}{r} 10 \\ -\ 7 \\ \hline \end{array}$$

- - - - - - - - -

How many are left? _____

6.

$$\begin{array}{r} 7 \\ -\ 2 \\ \hline \end{array}$$

- - - - - - - - -

How many are left? _____

7.

$$\begin{array}{r} 6 \\ -\ 3 \\ \hline \end{array}$$

- - - - - - - - -

How many are left? _____

Name_____ Date_____

Circle the correct number sentence.

1.

9 – 3 = 6

$\big(10 - 3 = 7\big)$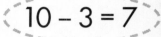

2.

8 – 6 = 2

10 – 8 = 2

3.

9 – 6 = 3

10 – 6 = 4

4.

7 – 5 = 2

10 – 5 = 5

5.

8 – 4 = 4

9 – 4 = 5

Name_____ Date_____

Cross out and subtract.

1.
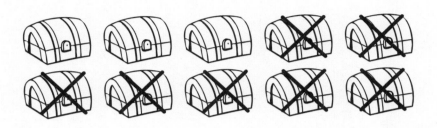

$$\begin{array}{r} 10 \\ -\ 7 \\ \hline \end{array}$$

3

2.

$$\begin{array}{r} 6 \\ -\ 1 \\ \hline \end{array}$$

3.

$$\begin{array}{r} 8 \\ -\ 6 \\ \hline \end{array}$$

4.
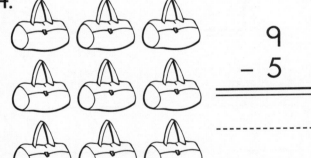

$$\begin{array}{r} 9 \\ -\ 5 \\ \hline \end{array}$$

5.

$$\begin{array}{r} 10 \\ -\ 4 \\ \hline \end{array}$$

6.

$$\begin{array}{r} 7 \\ -\ 6 \\ \hline \end{array}$$

Name_____ Date_____

Subtract.

1.

$$\begin{array}{r} 6 \\ -\ 6 \\ \hline \end{array}$$
- - - - - - - -
_____

$$\begin{array}{r} 8 \\ -\ 5 \\ \hline \end{array}$$
- - - - - - - -
_____

$$\begin{array}{r} 4 \\ -\ 1 \\ \hline \end{array}$$
- - - - - - - -
_____

$$\begin{array}{r} 9 \\ -\ 4 \\ \hline \end{array}$$
- - - - - - - -
_____

2.

$$\begin{array}{r} 5 \\ -\ 5 \\ \hline \end{array}$$
- - - - - - - -
_____

$$\begin{array}{r} 7 \\ -\ 3 \\ \hline \end{array}$$
- - - - - - - -
_____

$$\begin{array}{r} 9 \\ -\ 1 \\ \hline \end{array}$$
- - - - - - - -
_____

$$\begin{array}{r} 3 \\ -\ 2 \\ \hline \end{array}$$
- - - - - - - -
_____

3.

$$\begin{array}{r} 8 \\ -\ 4 \\ \hline \end{array}$$
- - - - - - - -
_____

$$\begin{array}{r} 2 \\ -\ 0 \\ \hline \end{array}$$
- - - - - - - -
_____

$$\begin{array}{r} 10 \\ -\ 6 \\ \hline \end{array}$$
- - - - - - - -
_____

$$\begin{array}{r} 7 \\ -\ 5 \\ \hline \end{array}$$
- - - - - - - -
_____

Subtraction Facts to 10 (III)

Name_____ Date_____

Subtract.

$$\begin{array}{r} 3 \\ -1 \\ \hline 2 \end{array}$$

1.

$$\begin{array}{r} 10 \\ -7 \\ \hline \end{array}$$
$$\begin{array}{r} 9 \\ -6 \\ \hline \end{array}$$
$$\begin{array}{r} 5 \\ -5 \\ \hline \end{array}$$
$$\begin{array}{r} 4 \\ -1 \\ \hline \end{array}$$

2.

$$\begin{array}{r} 8 \\ -3 \\ \hline \end{array}$$
$$\begin{array}{r} 7 \\ -4 \\ \hline \end{array}$$
$$\begin{array}{r} 10 \\ -5 \\ \hline \end{array}$$
$$\begin{array}{r} 2 \\ -1 \\ \hline \end{array}$$

3.

$$\begin{array}{r} 5 \\ -2 \\ \hline \end{array}$$
$$\begin{array}{r} 9 \\ -7 \\ \hline \end{array}$$
$$\begin{array}{r} 8 \\ -5 \\ \hline \end{array}$$
$$\begin{array}{r} 6 \\ -2 \\ \hline \end{array}$$

Name_____ Date_____

Subtract.

1.

$$\begin{array}{r} 10 \\ -7 \\ \hline \end{array} \qquad \begin{array}{r} 8 \\ -6 \\ \hline \end{array} \qquad \begin{array}{r} 9 \\ -5 \\ \hline \end{array} \qquad \begin{array}{r} 7 \\ -3 \\ \hline \end{array} \qquad \begin{array}{r} 2 \\ -0 \\ \hline \end{array}$$

2.

$$\begin{array}{r} 9 \\ -9 \\ \hline \end{array} \qquad \begin{array}{r} 4 \\ -2 \\ \hline \end{array} \qquad \begin{array}{r} 9 \\ -7 \\ \hline \end{array} \qquad \begin{array}{r} 9 \\ -6 \\ \hline \end{array} \qquad \begin{array}{r} 9 \\ -2 \\ \hline \end{array}$$

3.

$$\begin{array}{r} 3 \\ -3 \\ \hline \end{array} \qquad \begin{array}{r} 8 \\ -8 \\ \hline \end{array} \qquad \begin{array}{r} 8 \\ -6 \\ \hline \end{array} \qquad \begin{array}{r} 6 \\ -3 \\ \hline \end{array} \qquad \begin{array}{r} 7 \\ -4 \\ \hline \end{array}$$

4.

$$\begin{array}{r} 10 \\ -2 \\ \hline \end{array} \qquad \begin{array}{r} 5 \\ -4 \\ \hline \end{array} \qquad \begin{array}{r} 7 \\ -5 \\ \hline \end{array} \qquad \begin{array}{r} 5 \\ -3 \\ \hline \end{array} \qquad \begin{array}{r} 6 \\ -5 \\ \hline \end{array}$$

Name_____ Date_____

Subtract. Then add to check.

1.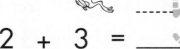

   $5 - 3 = $ _____ 2 _____   ✔ $2 + 3 = $ _____ 5 _____

2.

   $9 - 5 = $ _____   ✔ $4 + 5 = $ _____

3.

   $6 - 4 = $ _____   ✔ $2 + 4 = $ _____

4.

   $10 - 3 = $ _____   ✔ $7 + 3 = $ _____

5.

   $9 - 6 = $ _____   ✔ $3 + 6 = $ _____

Name_____ Date_____

$$4 + 3 = \underline{7}$$

○ 5
○ 6
● 7

Solve. Then fill in the circle next to the correct answer.

1. $3 + 1 = \underline{}$
○ 4
○ 5
○ 6

2. $5 - 3 = \underline{}$
○ 4
○ 3
○ 2

3. $10 - 9 = \underline{}$
○ 3
○ 2
○ 1

4. $2 + 2 = \underline{}$
○ 2
○ 3
○ 4

5. $8 - 4 = \underline{}$
○ 4
○ 3
○ 2

6. $6 + 3 = \underline{}$
○ 9
○ 10
○ 11

7. $7 + 2 = \underline{}$
○ 7
○ 8
○ 9

8. $9 - 4 = \underline{}$
○ 6
○ 5
○ 4

Addition and Subtraction Practice (II)

Name_____ Date_____

$$\begin{array}{r} 2 \\ + 7 \\ \hline 9 \end{array}$$

○ 8
● 9
○ 10

GREAT JOB!

Solve. Then fill in the circle next to the correct answer.

1.
$$\begin{array}{r} 7 \\ - 4 \\ \hline \end{array}$$
○ 4
○ 3
○ 2

2.
$$\begin{array}{r} 4 \\ + 5 \\ \hline \end{array}$$
○ 8
○ 9
○ 10

3.
$$\begin{array}{r} 5 \\ + 3 \\ \hline \end{array}$$
○ 6
○ 7
○ 8

4.
$$\begin{array}{r} 8 \\ - 7 \\ \hline \end{array}$$
○ 2
○ 1
○ 0

5.
$$\begin{array}{r} 10 \\ - 6 \\ \hline \end{array}$$
○ 6
○ 5
○ 4

6.
$$\begin{array}{r} 2 \\ + 1 \\ \hline \end{array}$$
○ 2
○ 3
○ 4

7.
$$\begin{array}{r} 3 \\ + 7 \\ \hline \end{array}$$
○ 10
○ 11
○ 12

8.
$$\begin{array}{r} 5 \\ - 5 \\ \hline \end{array}$$
○ 0
○ 5
○ 10

Name_____ Date_____

Read each problem. Write the answer.

1. Rita sent 3 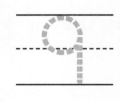s.

   Rob sent 6 s.

   How many s in all?

_____
_ _ _ _ _ _ _ 9
_____

---

2. Kate bought 6 s.

   Ken bought 2 s.

   How many s in all?

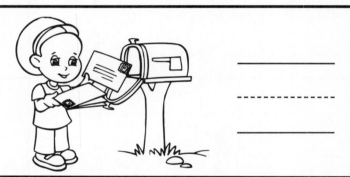

_____
_ _ _ _ _ _ _
_____

---

3. Liz has 4 s.

   Len has 3 s.

   How many s in all?

_____
_ _ _ _ _ _ _
_____

---

4. Zack has 2 s.

   Matt has 2 s.

   How many s in all?

_____
_ _ _ _ _ _ _
_____

Name_____ Date_____

Read each problem. Write the answer.

1. Erin has 4 s.
   Mary has 2 🐟s.

   How many 🐟s in all? _____

2. Bob has 2 🐸s.
   David has 3 🐸s.

   How many 🐸s in all? _____

3. Susie picked 7 🌼s.
   Jane picked 2 🌼s.

   How many 🌼s in all? _____

4. John has 5 🚗s.
   Ed has 3 🚗s.

   How many 🚗s in all? _____

5. Jenny has 3 🧸s.
   Joey has 1 🧸s.

   How many 🧸s in all? _____

Subtraction Word Problems (I)

Name_____ Date_____

Read each problem. Write the answer.

1. 4 🧸s on the 🪑.
   3 🧸s fall off.

   How many 🧸s are left? _____

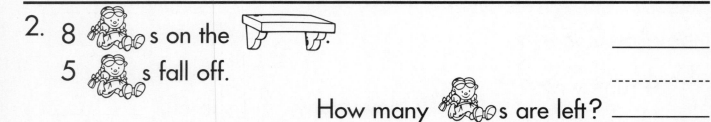

2. 8 🪆s on the 🪑.
   5 🪆s fall off.

   How many 🪆s are left? _____

3. 8 ⚾s on the 🪑.
   3 ⚾s roll off.

   How many ⚾s are left? _____

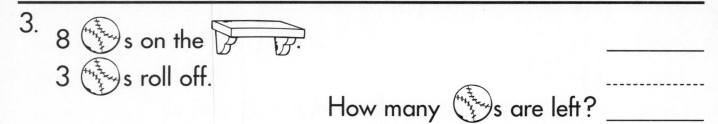

4. 6 🚗s on the 🪑.
   4 🚗s roll off.

   How many 🚗s are left? _____

5. 10 🔝s on the 🪑.
   5 🔝s fall off.

   How many 🔝s are left? _____

Subtraction Word Problems (II)

Name_____ Date_____

Read each problem. Write the answer.

1. 7 s.
    5 fly away.
    How many are left?

    7 − 5 = _____

2. 5 s.
    4 run away.
    How many are left?

    5 − 4 = _____

3. 9 s.
    3 go out.
    How many are left?

    9 − 3 = _____

4. 10 s.
    7 get picked.
    How many are left?

    10 − 7 = _____

5. 8 s.
    4 are eaten.
    How many are left?

    8 − 4 = _____

Name_____ Date_____

Read each problem. Write the answer.

1.

4 🐞 s.
2 more 🐞 s come.   How many 🐞 s in all? _____

2.

8 🐟 s.
4 🐟 s swim away.   How many 🐟 s are left? _____

3.

3 🐱 s.
3 more 🐱 s come.   How many 🐱 s in all? _____

4.

4 🐕 s.
5 more 🐕 s come.   How many 🐕 s in all? _____

5.

6 🐷 s.
2 🐷 s run away.   How many s are left? _____

Name_____   Date_____

Match.

12	
13	
11	
17	
18	
15	

Addition: Sets (1)

Name_____ Date_____

Count. Write how many.

1.

in all

9 + 9 = 18

2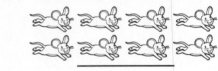

in all

_____ + _____ = _____

3.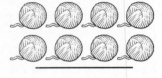

in all

_____ + _____ = _____

4.

in all

_____ + _____ = _____

5.

in all

_____ + _____ = _____

Addition: Sets (II)

Name_____ Date_____

Write how many.

1.
$$\begin{array}{r} 9 \\ + 8 \\ \hline \end{array}$$

_____ 7 _____

_____ in all

2.
$$\begin{array}{r} 8 \\ + 7 \\ \hline \end{array}$$

- - - - - - - - - -

_____ in all

3.
$$\begin{array}{r} 8 \\ + 9 \\ \hline \end{array}$$

- - - - - - - - - -

_____ in all

4.
$$\begin{array}{r} 9 \\ + 7 \\ \hline \end{array}$$

- - - - - - - - - -

_____ in all

5.
$$\begin{array}{r} 6 \\ + 9 \\ \hline \end{array}$$

- - - - - - - - - -

_____ in all

6.
$$\begin{array}{r} 6 \\ + 7 \\ \hline \end{array}$$

- - - - - - - - - -

_____ in all

7.
$$\begin{array}{r} 7 \\ + 7 \\ \hline \end{array}$$

- - - - - - - - - -

_____ in all

Name_____ Date_____

Add to find the sums.

1.

   9   +   9   = $\mathbf{18}$

2.    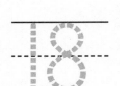   _____

   9 + 8 = _____   9 + 7 = _____

3. 3 + 8 = _____   9 + 3 = _____   8 + 5 = _____

4. 8 + 4 = _____   7 + 7 = _____   9 + 6 = _____

5. 8 + 8 = _____   9 + 2 = _____   5 + 7 = _____

6. 8 + 6 = _____   4 + 7 = _____   6 + 6 = _____

Name_____ Date_____

$$\begin{array}{r} 10 \\ +\ 8 \\ \hline 18 \end{array}$$

Add to find the sums.

1.

| $\begin{array}{r}9\\+8\\\hline\end{array}$ | $\begin{array}{r}9\\+2\\\hline\end{array}$ | $\begin{array}{r}9\\+9\\\hline\end{array}$ | $\begin{array}{r}6\\+8\\\hline\end{array}$ | $\begin{array}{r}7\\+5\\\hline\end{array}$ |

2.

| $\begin{array}{r}6\\+9\\\hline\end{array}$ | $\begin{array}{r}7\\+6\\\hline\end{array}$ | $\begin{array}{r}9\\+5\\\hline\end{array}$ | $\begin{array}{r}8\\+8\\\hline\end{array}$ | $\begin{array}{r}6\\+6\\\hline\end{array}$ |

3.

| $\begin{array}{r}3\\+8\\\hline\end{array}$ | $\begin{array}{r}5\\+8\\\hline\end{array}$ | $\begin{array}{r}7\\+4\\\hline\end{array}$ | $\begin{array}{r}4\\+8\\\hline\end{array}$ | $\begin{array}{r}7\\+7\\\hline\end{array}$ |

Name_____ Date_____

Add to complete the targets.

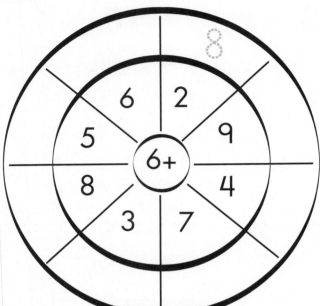

Addition Practice

Name_____ Date_____

○○○○○○○ ○○○○

7 + 4 = 11

Write the missing number.

1.

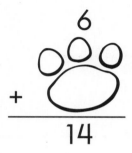

6		8	
+	+ 9	+	+ 9
14	12	13	17

2.

		9	9
+ 8	+ 6	+	+
16	15	18	13

3.

3		5	
+	+ 7	+	+ 7
11	13	15	14

Name_____ Date_____

Add.

1.

5	4	3	3	3
3	1	4	2	4
+ 6	+ 9	+ 8	+ 7	+ 5

2.

4	3	2	6	5
4	6	5	1	2
+ 9	+ 7	+ 3	+ 4	+ 6

Adding Three Numbers (II)

Name_____ Date_____

Add.

1.
   6   3   5   3   6
   2   2   3   3   1
+ 1   + 5   + 4   + 3   + 5

2.
   4   7   2   8   5
   1   2   4   1   1
+ 8   + 5   + 6   + 2   + 3

3.
   7   2   3   4   5
   1   3   6   4   2
+ 4   + 6   + 4   + 4   + 6

Name_____ Date_____

Subtract.

1.

    $15 - 8 = \underline{7}$

2. $14 - 9 = \underline{}$

3. $11 - 8 = \underline{}$

4. $18 - 9 = \underline{}$

5. $17 - 9 = \underline{}$

Name_____ Date_____

Cross out and subtract.

1.

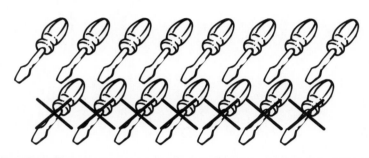

$$\begin{array}{r} 15 \\ -\ 7 \\ \hline \end{array}$$

8

2.

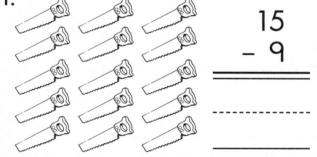

$$\begin{array}{r} 16 \\ -\ 8 \\ \hline \end{array}$$

3.

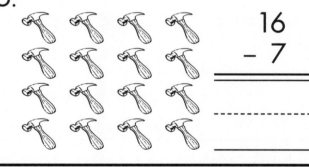

$$\begin{array}{r} 18 \\ -\ 9 \\ \hline \end{array}$$

4.

$$\begin{array}{r} 15 \\ -\ 9 \\ \hline \end{array}$$

5.

$$\begin{array}{r} 16 \\ -\ 7 \\ \hline \end{array}$$

6.

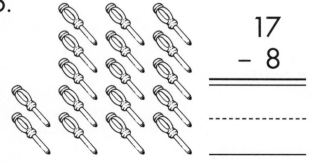

$$\begin{array}{r} 17 \\ -\ 8 \\ \hline \end{array}$$

7.

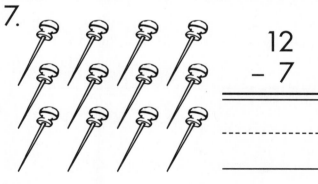

$$\begin{array}{r} 12 \\ -\ 7 \\ \hline \end{array}$$

Name_____ Date_____

Subtract.

1.

18	13	17	15
− 9	− 8	− 9	− 7

2.

14	15	16	11
− 8	− 9	− 8	− 2

3.

13	10	14	16
− 4	− 7	− 7	− 9

Name_____ Date_____

Unit 2

Subtract. Then match the problems with the same answers.

10 – 7 = _____

15 – 8 = _____

12 – 6 = _____

10 – 5 = _____

17 – 9 = _____

11 – 7 = _____

15 – 9 = _____

16 – 8 = _____

14 – 9 = _____

14 – 7 = _____

13 – 9 = _____

11 – 8 = _____

Subtraction Facts to 18 (III)

Name _____ Date _____

Subtract. Then use the code to color the quilt.

2 = red	4 = yellow	6 = blue	8 = pink
3 = orange	5 = green	7 = purple	9 = brown

1.
11 − 6	17 − 8	13 − 7	11 − 4	14 − 5	13 − 8	18 − 9

2.
16 − 7	14 − 6		13 − 9	12 − 3	13 − 5	15 − 7

3.
	13 − 4	14 − 8	15 − 6	11 − 6		

4.
11 − 2		11 − 3	12 − 5		11 − 7	12 − 9

5.
11 − 5	17 − 9	16 − 8		14 − 7		11 − 8

Subtraction Practice

Name_____ Date_____

Write the missing number.

1.

14
− ___
6

12
− ___
9

− 5
7

10
− ___
7

2.
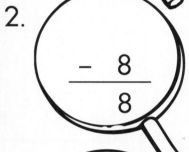
− 8
8

18
− ___
9

13
− ___
6

− 4
8

3.
17
− ___
8

− 7
4

14
− ___
9

9
− ___
5

4.
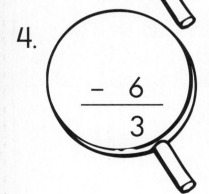
− 6
3

10
− ___
8

14
− ___
7

− 6
5

Name_____ Date_____

Subtract. Then add to check.

1.

$13 - 9 =$ -------------- ✔ -------------- $+ 9 = 13$

2.

$12 - 5 =$ -------------- ✔ -------------- $+ 5 = 12$

3.

$16 - 7 =$ -------------- ✔ -------------- $+ 7 = 16$

4.

$11 - 3 =$ -------------- ✔ -------------- $+ 3 = 11$

5.

$14 - 8 =$ -------------- ✔ -------------- $+ 8 = 14$

6.

$18 - 9 =$ -------------- ✔ -------------- $+ 9 = 18$

Name_____ Date_____

Solve the problems. If the answer is correct, circle it. If it is incorrect, change it to make it correct.

1.

7	15	18	8
+ 6	− 9	− 9	+ 3
12	6	8	11

2.

13	6	14	16
− 4	+ 5	− 7	− 8
9	11	8	9

3.

6	9	12	17
+ 8	+ 9	− 5	− 8
14	17	8	9

4.

10	14	4	7
− 3	− 7	+ 7	+ 8
6	7	12	16

Addition and Subtraction Practice

Name_____ Date_____

$8 + 3 = 11$

○ 10
◉ 11
○ 12

Solve. Then fill in the circle next to the correct answer.

1.

$13 - 7 =$ _____

○ 8
○ 7
○ 6

2.

$2 + 9 =$ _____

○ 9
○ 10
○ 11

2.

$5 + 6 =$ _____

○ 11
○ 12
○ 13

3.

$12 - 7 =$ _____

○ 5
○ 4
○ 3

4.

$15 - 8 =$ _____

○ 8
○ 7
○ 6

5.

$8 + 6 =$ _____

○ 12
○ 13
○ 14

6.

$7 + 4 =$ _____

○ 10
○ 11
○ 12

7.

$16 - 8 =$ _____

○ 9
○ 8
○ 7

Name_____ Date_____

Read each problem. Write the answer.

1.

Kim has 5 s.

She got 6 more s.

How many s does she have now?

```
   5
 + 6
------
- - - -
_____
```

2.

Rick found 8 s.

Pam found 7 s.

How many s did they find in all?

```
   8
 + 7
------
- - - -
_____
```

3.

Matt has 6 s.

Rob has 9 s.

How many s do they have in all?

```
   6
 + 9
------
- - - -
_____
```

4.

Pat has 7 s.

Her mother gave her 4 more.

How many s does she have now?

```
   7
 + 4
------
- - - -
_____
```

Addition Word Problems (II)

Name_____ Date_____

Read each problem. Write the answer.

1.

Ryan saw 7 ✈s.

Then he saw 6 more ✈s.

How many ✈s did he see in all?

$$\begin{array}{r} 7 \\ + 6 \\ \hline \end{array}$$

_____

2.

Nick collected 8 🍃s.

He found 3 more 🍃s.

How many 🍃s did he have in all?

$$\begin{array}{r} 8 \\ + 3 \\ \hline \end{array}$$

_____

3.

Ashley planted 9 🍅s.

Frank planted 4 🍅s.

How many s were planted in all?

$$\begin{array}{r} 9 \\ + 4 \\ \hline \end{array}$$

_____

4.

Kyle has 9 🎈s.

His dad gave him 8 more 🎈s.

How many 🎈s does he have now?

$$\begin{array}{r} 9 \\ + 8 \\ \hline \end{array}$$

_____

Subtraction Word Problems (I)

Name_____ Date_____

Read each problem. Write the answer.

1.

I had 11 ◯s.

5 ◯s popped.

How many ◯s are left?

$$\begin{array}{r} 11 \\ -\ 8 \\ \hline \end{array}$$

2.

I saw 13 🦆s.

4 🦆s swam away.

How many 🦆s are left?

$$\begin{array}{r} 13 \\ -\ 4 \\ \hline \end{array}$$

3.

I have 9 🪙s.

I need 16 🪙s.

How many more 🪙s do I need?

$$\begin{array}{r} 16 \\ -\ 9 \\ \hline \end{array}$$

4.

I had 16 🪐s.

I gave away 8 🪐s.

How many 🪐s do I have left?

$$\begin{array}{r} 16 \\ -\ 8 \\ \hline \end{array}$$

Name_____ Date_____

Read each problem. Write the answer.

1.

Hohn had 17 s.

He gave 8 s to Ray.

How many s does John have left?

17
− 8
_____
- - - - - - -
_____

2.

Mary had 16 s.

She broke 7 s.

How many s does she have left?

16
− 7
_____
- - - - - - -
_____

3.

There were 12 s.

4 s hopped away.

How many s are left?

12
− 4
_____
- - - - - - -
_____

4.

Mrs. Gray's class had 15 s.

They ate 9 s.

How many s are left?

15
− 9
_____
- - - - - - -
_____

Addition and Subtraction Word Problems

Name_____   Date_____

Read each problem. Write a number sentence and solve.

1. Farmer Dan had 13 corn plants in the field. He harvested 6 of them. How many corn plants are left in the field?

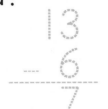

$$\begin{array}{r} 13 \\ -6 \\ \hline 7 \end{array}$$

2. Tara bought 9 petunias and 7 pansies. How many flowers did she buy altogether?

_____

3. Marci picked 15 flowers from the garden. She put 8 flowers in a vase and gave the rest away. How many flowers did Marci give away?

_____

4. Keisha picked 12 tomatoes from the garden. She used 5 tomatoes for a sauce and saved the rest for salad. How many tomatoes did Keisha save?

_____

5. Evan planted 5 green pepper plants and 9 red pepper plants. How many pepper plants did he plant altogether?

_____

6. Carlos picked 3 red apples and 9 green apples. How many apples did he pick altogether?

_____

Two-Dimensional Shapes (1)

Name_____ Date_____

square   circle   triangle   rectangle

Match.

Name_____ Date_____

Trace each shape.

square   circle   triangle   rectangle

Write **S** on all the squares.
Write **T** on all the triangles.

Write **C** on all the circles.
Write **R** on all the rectangles.

Name_____ Date_____

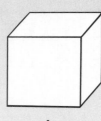

cube

cylinder

cone

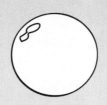

sphere

Match.

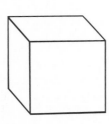

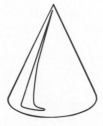

Three-Dimensional Shapes (II)

Name_____ Date_____

Trace each shape.

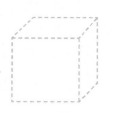 

cube   cylinder   cone   sphere

Color the **cubes** yellow.
Color the **cones** blue.

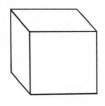   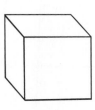 

   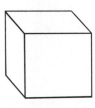 

Color the **cylinders** green.
Color the **spheres** orange.

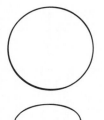 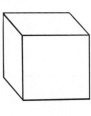 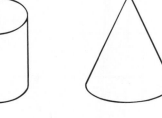  

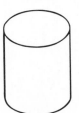   

Sets (1)

Name _____ Date _____

A set is a group of things with something in common.

Circle the things that belong in each set.

1.

2.

3.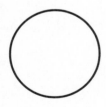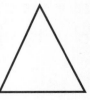

4.

Sets (II)

Color the things that belong in each set.

1.

2.

3.

4.

Unit 3

Name_____ Date_____

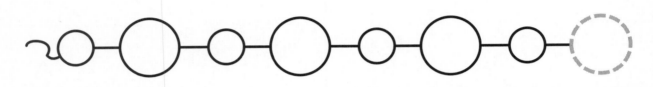

Draw the shape that comes next. Color the shapes to make a pattern.

1.

2.
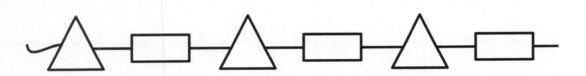

3.
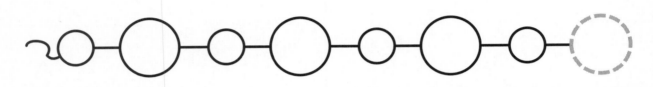

4.
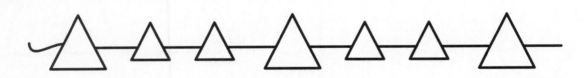

5.
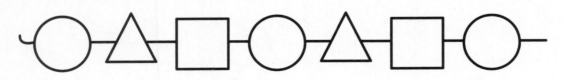

6.
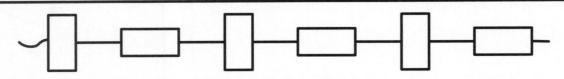

Shape Patterns (II)

Name_____ Date_____

Draw the missing shape. Color the shapes to make a pattern.

1.

2.

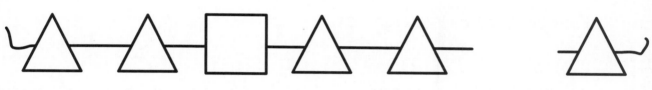

3.

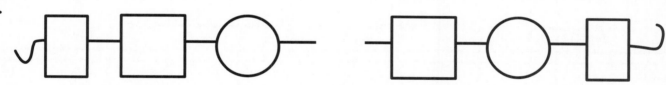

4.

5.

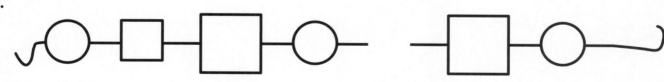

6.

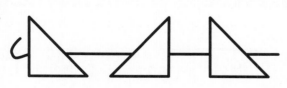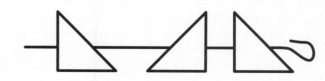

Congruent Shapes

Name_____ Date_____

Congruent shapes are the same shape and size.

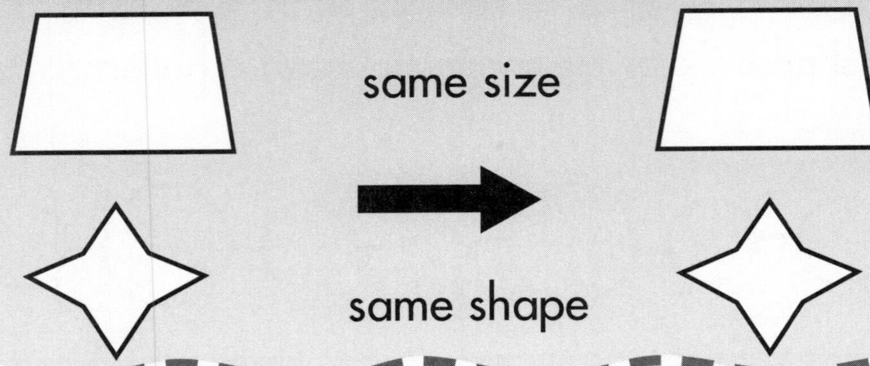

same size

same shape

Color the shapes that are **congruent**.

1.

2.

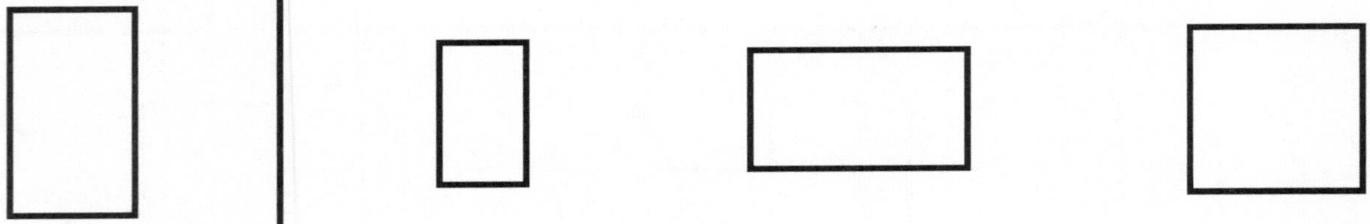

3.

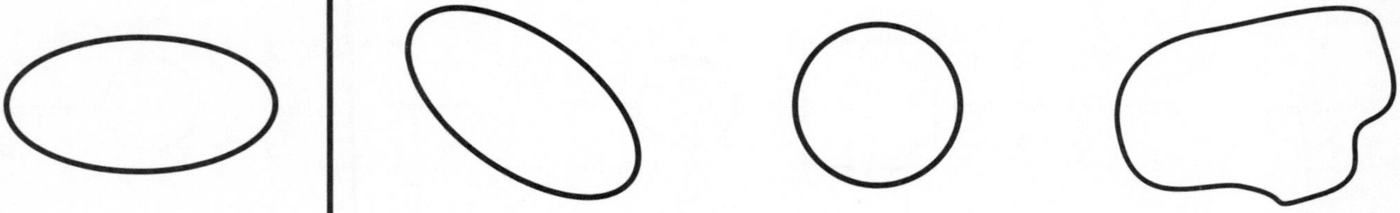

4.

Shape and Pattern Practice

Name_____ Date_____

1. Color the **circle.**

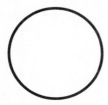

2. Color the **rectangle**.

3. Draw what comes next. Color a pattern.

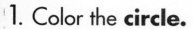

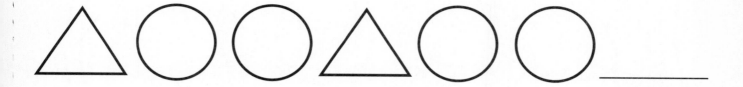

4. Color the shapes that are **congruent**.

5. Color the **cube.**

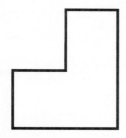 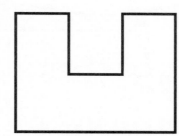

6. Color the **cone**.

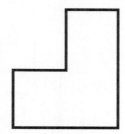 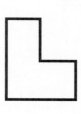

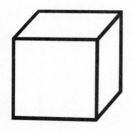   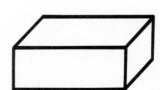

Counting

Name_____ Date_____

Count the shapes. Write how many.

1. How many ▢s? _____

2. How many △s? _____

3. How many ○s? _____

4. How many ▭s? _____

Bar Graphs (1)

Name_____ Date_____

Color the graph.

Show how many of each shape you counted on page 60.

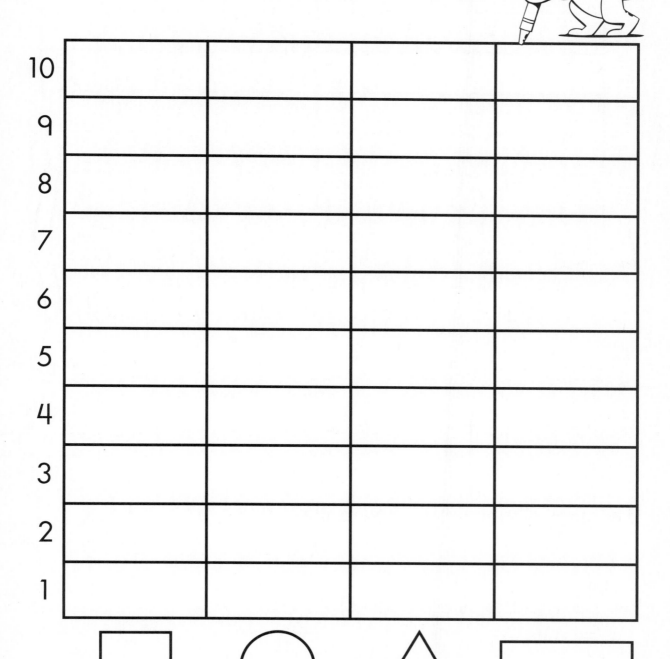

Name_____ Date_____

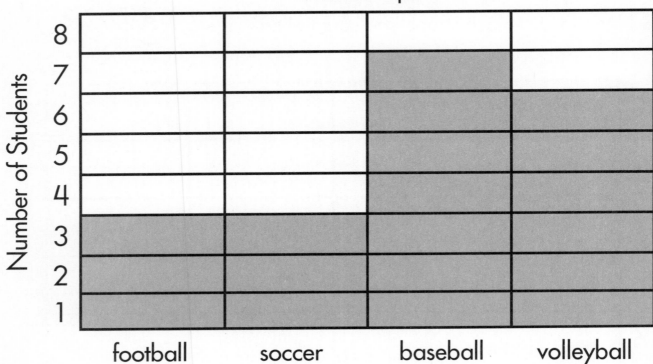

Favorite Sport

Use the graph to answer the questions.

_____

_____

1. How many students play football?

_____

_____

2. How many students play baseball?

_____

_____

3. How many students play soccer?

_____

_____

4. How many students play volleyball?

_____

Bar Graphs (III)

Name_____ Date_____

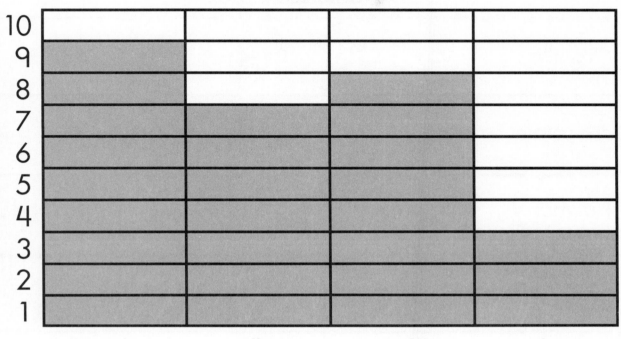

Favorite Cake

Use the graph to answer the questions.

_____

1. How many students like yellow cake? _____

_____

2. How many students like white cake? _____

_____

3. How many students like chocolate cake? _____

_____

4. How many students like marble cake? _____

Picture Graphs

Name_____ Date_____

Favorite Ice Cream

vanilla	🍦🍦🍦
chocolate	🍦🍦🍦🍦🍦
strawberry	🍦
chocolate chip	🍦🍦🍦🍦

Use the graph to answer the questions.

1. How many students like chocolate ice cream? _____

2. How many students like vanilla ice cream? _____

3. How many students like chocolate chip ice cream? _____

4. How many students like strawberry ice cream?

Name_____ Date_____

Use the graphs to answer the questions.

Dinner Time

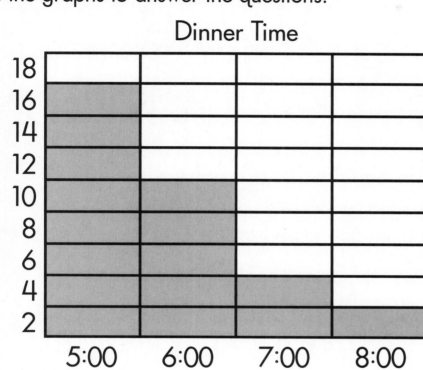

How many said...

_____

- - - - - - - - - -

1. 7:00? _____

- - - - - - - - - -

2. 6:00? _____

- - - - - - - - - -

3. 8:00? _____

- - - - - - - - - -

4. 5:00? _____

Favorite Pizza

pepperoni	🍕🍕🍕🍕🍕
cheese	🍕🍕🍕🍕
mushroom	🍕
sausage	🍕🍕🍕

🍕 = 1 child

How many said...

_____

- - - - - - - - - -

5. pepperoni? _____

- - - - - - - - - -

6. sausage? _____

- - - - - - - - - -

7. mushroom? _____

- - - - - - - - - -

8. cheese? _____

One Half

1 part shaded
2 equal parts

½ or one half
is shaded.

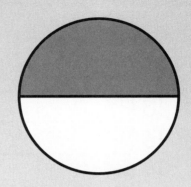

Two equal parts are halves.

Circle the shapes that show halves. Color **½** of each shape.

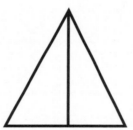
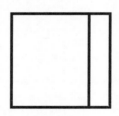

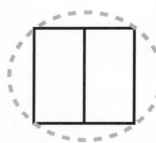
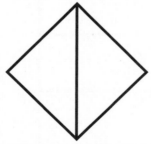
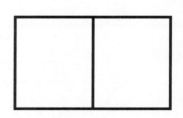

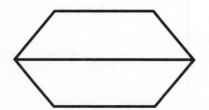
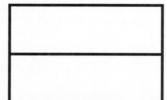
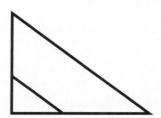

One Fourth

Name_____ Date_____

$\dfrac{1}{4}$ part shaded
equal parts

$\dfrac{1}{4}$ or one fourth
is shaded.

Four equal parts are fourths.

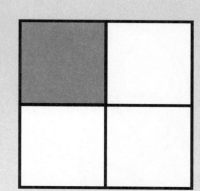

Circle the shapes that show fourths. Color $\dfrac{1}{4}$ of each shape.

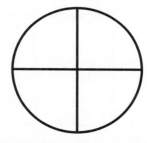 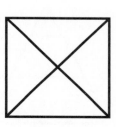 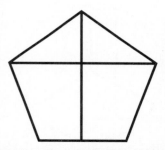

 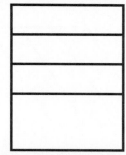 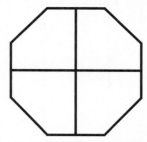

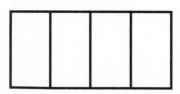 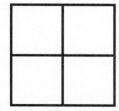 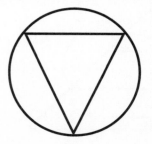

One Third

$\frac{1 \text{ part shaded}}{3 \text{ equal parts}}$

$\frac{1}{3}$ or one third is shaded.

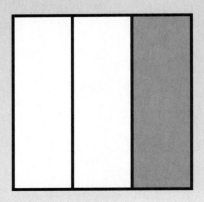

Three equal parts are thirds.

Circle the shapes that show thirds. Color $\frac{1}{3}$ of each shape.

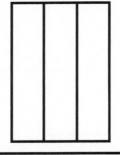

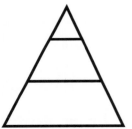

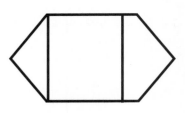

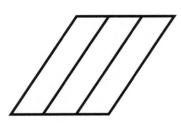

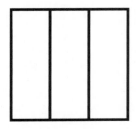

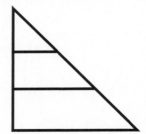

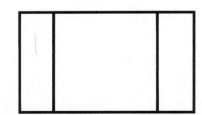

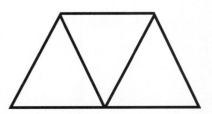

Name_____ Date_____

Color one part. Circle the fraction that names the colored part.

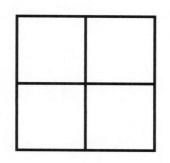

$\frac{1}{2}$ $\frac{1}{3}$ $\frac{1}{4}$

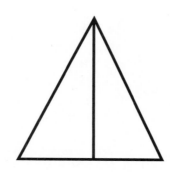

$\frac{1}{2}$ $\frac{1}{3}$ $\frac{1}{4}$

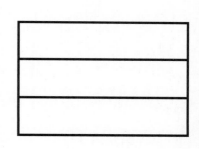

$\frac{1}{2}$ $\frac{1}{3}$ $\frac{1}{4}$

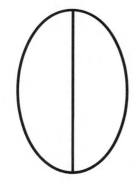

$\frac{1}{2}$ $\frac{1}{3}$ $\frac{1}{4}$

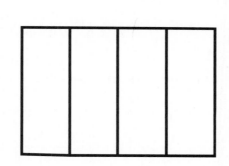

$\frac{1}{2}$ $\frac{1}{3}$ $\frac{1}{4}$

$\frac{1}{2}$ $\frac{1}{3}$ $\frac{1}{4}$

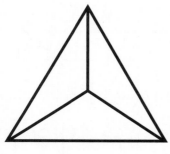

$\frac{1}{2}$ $\frac{1}{3}$ $\frac{1}{4}$

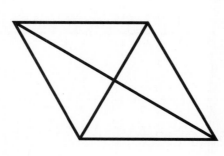

$\frac{1}{2}$ $\frac{1}{3}$ $\frac{1}{4}$

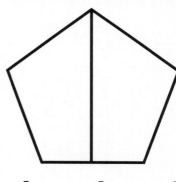

$\frac{1}{2}$ $\frac{1}{3}$ $\frac{1}{4}$

Tens and Ones

Name_____ Date_____

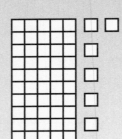 = | tens | ones |
|---|---|
| **5** | **6** |

56

Count the tens and ones. Write the number.

1.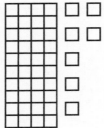

tens	ones

_____ tens _____ ones = _____

tens	ones

_____ tens _____ ones = _____

2.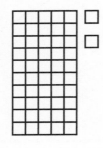

tens	ones

_____ tens _____ ones = _____

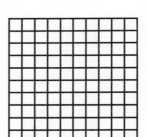

tens	ones

_____ tens _____ ones = _____

3.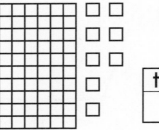

tens	ones

_____ tens _____ ones = _____

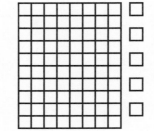 

tens	ones

_____ tens _____ ones = _____

Numbers: Expanded Form

Name_____ Date_____

Write the number.

1. 30 + 5 = _35__   80 + 2 = _____   70 + 1 = _____

2. 60 + 3 = _____   40 + 7 = _____   20 + 2 = _____

3. 10 + 9 = _____   90 + 1 = _____   50 + 6 = _____

4. 30 + 2 = _____   80 + 5 = _____   60 + 8 = _____

Write an addition sentence.

5. 49 = ___ + ___   26 = ___ + ___   15 = ___ + ___

6. 53 = ___ + ___   45 = ___ + ___   62 = ___ + ___

7. 74 = ___ + ___   80 = ___ + ___   79 = ___ + ___

8. 57 = ___ + ___   61 = ___ + ___   98 = ___ + ___

Name_____ Date_____

Match.

8 tens and 3 ones	97	50 + 8
5 tens and 8 ones	58	30 + 1
3 tens and 1 one	31	90 + 7
9 tens and 7 ones	26	80 + 9
8 tens and 9 ones	64	60 + 4
7 tens and 5 ones	83	20 + 6
6 tens and 4 ones	75	40 + 3
2 tens and 6 ones	89	10 + 7
1 ten and 7 ones	43	80 + 3
4 tens and 3 ones	17	70 + 5

Place Value Practice (II)

Name_____ Date_____

Count how many tens and ones. Write the number.

1.   ___ ___ = _____
   tens   ones

2.   ___ ___ = _____
   tens   ones

3.  ___ ___ = _____
   tens   ones

Unit 4

Write how many tens and ones.

4. 35 = _____ tens _____ ones   54 = _____ tens _____ ones

5. 81 = _____ tens _____ ones   29 = _____ tens _____ ones

Write the number.

6. 4 tens and 3 ones = _____   1 ten and 6 ones = _____

7. 6 tens and 0 ones = _____   9 tens and 9 ones = _____

Adding Ones and Tens (1)

Name_____ Date_____

tens	ones
3	0
+ 2	0
5	0

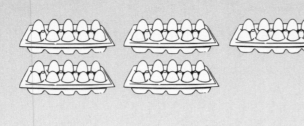

First add the ones. Then add then tens.

1.
tens	ones
4	0
+ 1	0
5	0

tens	ones
7	0
+ 2	0

2.
30	10	40	50	60	50
+ 30	+ 70	+ 30	+ 20	+ 30	+ 40

3.
60	50	80	40	10	40
+ 20	+ 30	+ 10	+ 20	+ 40	+ 40

Name_____ Date_____

Add. Then find the balloon with the same sum and color it.

1.
```
   34        21        51         5
 + 15      + 23      + 15      + 81
 _____    _____    _____    _____
```

2.
```
   60        43         7        21
 + 29      + 15      + 70      + 44
 _____    _____    _____    _____
```

3.
```
   27        32        42        21
 + 12      + 23      + 50      + 72
 _____    _____    _____    _____
```

4.
```
   53        62        43        91
 + 26      + 16      + 44       + 7
 _____    _____    _____    _____
```

Balloons:
49
44
92
86
79
93
89
58
65
78
39
55
66
98
87
77

Name_____ Date_____

Add.

Don't forget! Add the ones first.

1.
```
   26
 + 43
 ═════
```
```
   31
 + 42
 ═════
```
```
   20
 + 34
 ═════
```
```
   30
 +  9
 ═════
```

2.
```
   41
 + 57
 ═════
```
```
   52
 + 32
 ═════
```
```
   64
 + 11
 ═════
```
```
    7
 + 52
 ═════
```

3.
```
   26
 + 43
 ═════
```
```
   31
 + 42
 ═════
```
```
   20
 + 34
 ═════
```
```
   30
 +  9
 ═════
```

4.
```
   22
 + 17
 ═════
```
```
   30
 + 28
 ═════
```
```
   33
 + 14
 ═════
```
```
   24
 + 13
 ═════
```

Adding Three Numbers (1)

Name_____ Date_____

Add.

1.
```
   24        17
   10        61
 + 15      + 10
 ══════    ══════

 ------    ------
```

"Remember to add the ones and then the tens."

2.
```
   11        21        10        12        23
   13        30        35        21        32
 + 43      + 32      + 34      + 15      + 13
 ══════    ══════    ══════    ══════    ══════

 ------    ------    ------    ------    ------
```

3.
```
   13        31        64        27        30
   62        41        20        12        12
 + 24      + 20      + 13      + 50      + 54
 ══════    ══════    ══════    ══════    ══════

 ------    ------    ------    ------    ------
```

4.
```
   20        50        27        40        75
   30        12        12        31        11
 + 41      + 13      + 50      + 14      + 12
 ══════    ══════    ══════    ══════    ══════

 ------    ------    ------    ------    ------
```

Name_____ Date_____

Add.

1.
```
   26        33        36        13        52
   11        40        10        31        26
 + 52      + 15      + 22      + 30      + 10
```

2.
```
   14        41        70        16        10
   51        21        15        20        30
 + 24      + 11      + 13      + 30      + 25
```

3.
```
   22        10        27        37        15
   33        11        12        31        14
 + 44      + 12      + 40      + 21      + 60
```

4.
```
   70        50        44        16        61
   15        12        23        31        16
 + 12      + 24      + 32      + 52      + 11
```

Name _____ Date _____

tens	ones
3	8
− 2	3
1	5

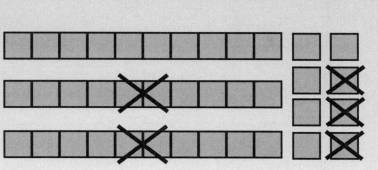

- -

First subtract the ones. Then subtract the tens.

1.

tens	ones
5	6
− 2	5

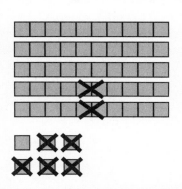

tens	ones
4	7
− 1	4

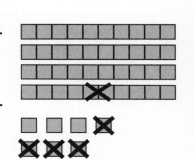

Unit 4

4.

39	65	98	73	84
− 28	− 21	− 40	− 43	− 72

4.

95	67	82	24	96
− 62	− 44	− 51	− 12	− 32

Name_____   Date_____

Subtract.

Don't forget! Subtract the ones, then the tens.

1.
$$48 - 24$$ $$97 - 62$$ $$99 - 81$$ $$87 - 73$$

2.
$$97 - 33$$ $$45 - 14$$ $$68 - 45$$ $$43 - 12$$

3.
$$67 - 35$$ $$66 - 24$$ $$79 - 42$$ $$98 - 56$$

4.
$$39 - 13$$ $$27 - 16$$ $$55 - 31$$ $$79 - 22$$

Name_____ Date_____

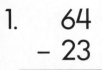

Subtract.

1.
```
   64        16        32        45        64
 - 23      -  6      - 11      - 13      - 23
 ======    ======    ======    ======    ======

 ------    ------    ------    ------    ------
```

2.
```
   81        93        78        49        59
 - 70      - 61      - 56      - 27      - 18
 ======    ======    ======    ======    ======

 ------    ------    ------    ------    ------
```

3.
```
   36        68        95        87        74
 -  3      - 34      - 14      - 43      - 63
 ======    ======    ======    ======    ======

 ------    ------    ------    ------    ------
```

4.
```
   98        58        47        60        89
 - 33      - 30      - 21      - 40      - 52
 ======    ======    ======    ======    ======

 ------    ------    ------    ------    ------
```

Name_____ Date_____

$$\begin{array}{r} 11 \\ + \ 3 \\ \hline 14 \end{array}$$

○ 12
○ 13
● 14

GREAT WORK!

Solve. Then fill in the circle next to the correct answer.

1.
$$\begin{array}{r} 23 \\ + \ 1 \\ \hline \end{array}$$
○ 23
○ 24
○ 25

2.
$$\begin{array}{r} 89 \\ - 43 \\ \hline \end{array}$$
○ 47
○ 46
○ 45

3.
$$\begin{array}{r} 65 \\ + \ 2 \\ \hline \end{array}$$
○ 60
○ 66
○ 67

4.
$$\begin{array}{r} 23 \\ + 41 \\ \hline \end{array}$$
○ 22
○ 46
○ 64

5.
$$\begin{array}{r} 54 \\ - \ 3 \\ \hline \end{array}$$
○ 52
○ 51
○ 50

6.
$$\begin{array}{r} 32 \\ - 11 \\ \hline \end{array}$$
○ 22
○ 21
○ 20

7.
$$\begin{array}{r} 60 \\ + 10 \\ \hline \end{array}$$
○ 7
○ 60
○ 70

8.
$$\begin{array}{r} 45 \\ - 22 \\ \hline \end{array}$$
○ 13
○ 23
○ 22

Name_____   Date_____

$$\begin{array}{r} 40 \\ -\ 20 \\ \hline 20 \end{array}$$

○ 30
● 20
○ 10

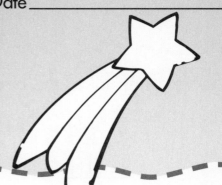

Solve. Then fill in the circle next to the correct answer.

1.
$$\begin{array}{r} 60 \\ -\ 20 \\ \hline \end{array}$$
○ 60
○ 50
○ 40

2.
$$\begin{array}{r} 40 \\ +\ 30 \\ \hline \end{array}$$
○ 47
○ 46
○ 45

3.
$$\begin{array}{r} 37 \\ -\ 5 \\ \hline \end{array}$$
○ 32
○ 31
○ 30

4.
$$\begin{array}{r} 64 \\ +\ 14 \\ \hline \end{array}$$
○ 50
○ 40
○ 30

5.
$$\begin{array}{r} 34 \\ +\ 24 \\ \hline \end{array}$$
○ 38
○ 58
○ 54

6.
$$\begin{array}{r} 82 \\ +\ 16 \\ \hline \end{array}$$
○ 98
○ 99
○ 88

7.
$$\begin{array}{r} 78 \\ -\ 53 \\ \hline \end{array}$$
○ 26
○ 25
○ 24

8.
$$\begin{array}{r} 55 \\ +\ 21 \\ \hline \end{array}$$
○ 65
○ 76
○ 56

Unit 4

Name_____ Date_____

Solve. Then fill in the circle next to the correct answer.

1.

$$\begin{array}{r} 25 \\ +\ 14 \\ \hline \end{array}$$

- ○ 49
- ○ 39
- ○ 31

2.

$$\begin{array}{r} 84 \\ -\ 61 \\ \hline \end{array}$$

- ○ 23
- ○ 24
- ○ 25

3.

$$\begin{array}{r} 73 \\ -\ 20 \\ \hline \end{array}$$

- ○ 90
- ○ 93
- ○ 53

4.

$$\begin{array}{r} 56 \\ +\ 23 \\ \hline \end{array}$$

- ○ 73
- ○ 79
- ○ 33

5.

$$\begin{array}{r} 66 \\ -\ 33 \\ \hline \end{array}$$

- ○ 33
- ○ 99
- ○ 22

6.

$$\begin{array}{r} 32 \\ +\ 46 \\ \hline \end{array}$$

- ○ 77
- ○ 79
- ○ 78

7.

$$\begin{array}{r} 48 \\ +\ 20 \\ \hline \end{array}$$

- ○ 28
- ○ 68
- ○ 78

8.

$$\begin{array}{r} 97 \\ -\ 11 \\ \hline \end{array}$$

- ○ 86
- ○ 88
- ○ 90

9.

$$\begin{array}{r} 26 \\ -\ 13 \\ \hline \end{array}$$

- ○ 12
- ○ 13
- ○ 18

10.

$$\begin{array}{r} 37 \\ +\ 32 \\ \hline \end{array}$$

- ○ 99
- ○ 74
- ○ 69

Addition Word Problems (I)

Name_____ Date_____

Read each problem.
Write a number sentence and solve.

1. One day, Mr. Perez sells 32 puffy animal stickers and 57 plain animal stickers. How many animal stickers does he sell that day?

_____

2. Mr. Perez orders 52 new shiny stickers and 26 new puffy stickers. How many new stickers does Mr. Perez order?

_____

3. Ms. Ross buys 87 car stickers and 12 happy face stickers. How many stickers does Ms. Ross buy?

_____

4. Julie's scout troop buys 31 puffy stickers and 48 shiny stickers. How many stickers does the troop buy?

_____

5. Mrs. Patel buys 24 "Good Work" stickers and 51 star stickers. How many stickers does Mrs. Patel buy?

_____

6. The Sticker Club buys 37 elephant stickers and 21 bear stickers. How many stickers does the club buy?

_____

Unit 4

Addition Word Problems (II)

Name_____ Date_____

Read each problem.
Write a number sentence and solve.

1. Manuel bought a truck and markers. How many tokens did he spend?

_____

2. Hunter bought two coloring books. How many tokens did he spend?

_____

3. Kameisha bought a doll and stickers. How many tokens did she spend?

_____

4. Nick bought stickers and a sticker book. How many tokens did he spend?

_____

5. Liz bought a coloring book and markers. How many tokens did she spend?

_____

6. Mai bought a stuffed bear and a coloring book. How many tokens did she spend?

_____

7. Who spent the most tokens?

_____

8. Who spent the fewest tokens?

_____

Name_____ Date_____

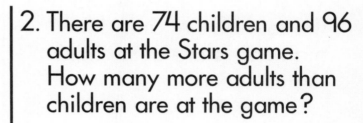

Read each problem.
Write a number sentence and solve.

1. There are 38 boys and 49 girls at the Stars game. How many more girls than boys are at the game?

_____

2. There are 74 children and 96 adults at the Stars game. How many more adults than children are at the game?

_____

3. Manny sells 42 sodas and 67 bottled waters. How many more bottled waters than sodas are sold?

_____

4. Jane sells 45 bags of peanuts and 95 hot dogs. How many more hot dogs than peanuts are sold?

_____

5. The Stars sell 56 pennants. Of those, 14 are small pennants and the rest are large pennants. How many large pennants are sold?

_____

6. The Stars play 65 games at home out of a total of 99 games. How many games are played away from home?

_____

Unit 4

Subtraction Word Problems (II)

Name_____ Date_____

Read each problem.
Write a number sentence and solve.

1. Of a total of 62 children at the fair, 30 are girls. How many boys are at the fair?

_____

2. There are 62 children and 41 adults at the fair. How many more children than adults are at the fair?

_____

3. Mr. Brown prepares 27 hamburgers, but he only sells 15 of them. How many hamburgers are not sold?

_____

4. Of 89 families that buy raffle tickets, only 47 of them win prizes. How many families do not win prizes?

_____

5. Amy sells 78 bags of popcorn. Of those, 36 are regular-size bags, and the rest are super-size. How many super-size bags of popcorn are sold?

_____

6. Mr. Chen had 38 school sweatshirts, but he sold 15 of them. How many school sweatshirts did Mr. Chen have left?

_____

Name_____ Date_____

Read each problem.
Write a number sentence and solve.

1. There were 85 students who went to the zoo. Only 42 of them were girls. How many boys went to the zoo?

_____

2. Cathy took 24 pictures while at the zoo. Her teacher took 41 pictures. How many pictures did they taken altogether?

_____

3. George counted 24 monkeys playing on the high wire. Then 13 more came out of their cave. How many monkeys were there altogether?

_____

4. 39 birds were spotted in the tree. After someone yelled, only 10 were left. How many birds flew away?

_____

5. The elephants had 55 visitors on Monday and 32 visitors on Tuesday. How many visitors did they have altogether?

_____

6. Mary bought 41 peanuts to feed the animals. She used 20 to feed the elephants. How many peanuts does she have left?

_____

Unit 4

Counting to 100

Write the numbers to finish the chart.

1	2			5			8		10
11		13				17		19	20
21			24	25				29	30
31		33			36		38	39	
	42		44			47			50
51				55	56				60
61			64			67		69	
71		73			76				80
	82			85			88		90
91			94		96			99	100

Odd and Even Numbers

Name_____ Date_____

Odd numbers end in **1, 3, 5, 7**, or **9**.

Even numbers end in **0**, **2**, **4**, **6**, or **8**.

Circle the **odd** numbers.

1.	12	17	43	96	25	34	51	60
2.	27	28	6	15	67	50	4	88
3.	11	9	6	24	30	22	23	91
4.	44	47	5	19	10	13	20	86

Circle the **even** numbers.

5.	75	80	93	52	46	33	73	90
6.	18	29	31	66	7	40	82	89
7.	2	21	49	53	50	78	81	35
8.	55	64	58	3	71	65	70	83

Count how many you circled for each. Write the number.

9. _____ odd numbers   10. _____ even numbers

Name_____ Date_____

```
  |        |        |        |
  25      26       27       28
```

26 comes **before 27**.

Circle the number that comes **before**.

1. I am before 37.
   What number am I?

   (36)   **38**   **47**

2. I am before 89.
   What number am I?

   90   **98**   **88**

3. I am before 17.
   What number am I?

   16   **18**   **37**

4. I am before 23.
   What number am I?

   25   **24**   **22**

5. I am before 50.
   What number am I?

   60   **49**   **51**

6. I am before 61.
   What number am I?

   67   **64**   **60**

7. I am before 98.
   What number am I?

   100   **99**   **97**

8. I am before 80.
   What number am I?

   81   **79**   **90**

Name_____ Date_____

56   **57**   **58**   59

58 comes **after 57**.

Write the number that comes **after**.

1.  9 ___   12 ___   19 ___

2. 23 ___   28 ___   30 ___

3. 36 ___   40 ___   44 ___

4. 49 ___   54 ___   61 ___

5. 66 ___   70 ___   78 ___

6. 87 ___   92 ___   99 ___

Unit 5

Number Order: Between

33   **34**   35

34 comes **between 33** and **35**.

Write the number that comes **between**.

1. 26 ___27___ 28   14 _____ 16

2. 51 _____ 53   68 _____ 70

3. 83 _____ 85   40 _____ 42

4. 32 _____ 34   95 _____ 97

5. 74 _____ 76   29 _____ 31

Name_____ Date_____

45. 54. 60.

The numbers from **least** to **greatest** are **45, 54, 60**.

Write each group of numbers from **least** to **greatest**.

1. 10   30   20

   10   20   30
   ___ ___ ___

3. 18   23   14

   ___ ___ ___

5. 45   48   52

   ___ ___ ___

7. 34   41   29

2. 75   57   68

   ___ ___ ___

4. 35   27   31

   ___ ___ ___

6. 67   82   53

   ___ ___ ___

8. 60   47   59

9. 90   68   77

   ___ ___ ___   ___ ___ ___   ___ ___ ___

Unit 5

Inequality Symbols

Name_____ Date_____

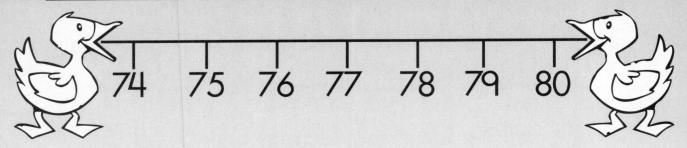

< means "is **less than**"   > means "is **greater than**"
76 < 78   77 > 75

Write **<** or **>** to complete each sentence.
Be sure the duck's mouth is open to the **greatest** number.

1. | 10 __>__ 9 | | 36 ____ 40 | | 18 ____ 81 |

2. | 80 ____ 68 | | 54 ____ 40 | | 16 ____ 71 |

3. | 36 ____ 39 | | 25 ____ 29 | | 50 ____ 49 |

5 | 27 ____ 72 | | 82 ____ 85 | | 71 ____ 79 |

5. | 60 ____ 59 | | 30 ____ 39 | | 48 ____ 50 |

6. | 39 ____ 31 | | 56 ____ 85 | | 19 ____ 21 |

Ordinal Numbers

Name_____ Date_____

	first	second	third	fourth	fifth	sixth	seventh	eighth	ninth	tenth
TOYS	1st	2nd	3rd	4th	5th	6th	7th	8th	9th	10th

Color the toy to show the ordinal number.

3rd	🗑	🗑	🗑	🗑	🗑	🗑
5th	🪁	🪁	🪁	🪁	🪁	🪁
4th	🥁	🥁	🥁	🥁	🥁	🥁
2nd	🧸	🧸	🧸	🧸	🧸	🧸	🧸	🧸
6th	🧍	🧍	🧍	🧍	🧍	🧍	🧍	🧍
9th	🚗	🚗	🚗	🚗	🚗	🚗	🚗	🚗	🚗	🚗
7th	✈	✈	✈	✈	✈	✈	✈	✈	✈	✈

Unit 5

Number Order Practice

Name_____ Date_____

Write the missing numbers.

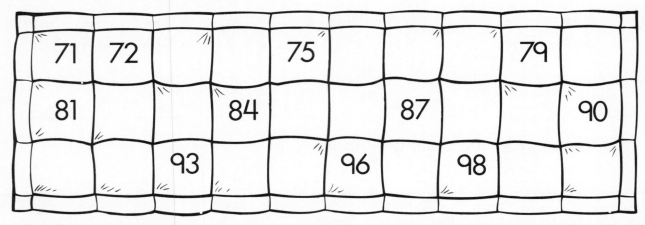

71	72			75				79	
81			84			87			90
		93			96		98		

Write the missing numbers.

4. 53 ____   ____ 20   36 ____ 38   49 ____

5. ____ 31   87 ____   12 ____ 14   ____ 75

Write **<** or **>** to complete each sentence.

6. | 79 ___ 80 | | 65 ___ 56 | | 41 ___ 38 | | 27 ___ 72 |

7. | 32 ___ 23 | | 87 ___ 90 | | 80 ___ 70 | | 55 ___ 52 |

Solve the riddles. Write the numbers.

8. I am an odd number between 40 and 50. You say me when you count by 5's. What number am I?

9. I am an even number greater than 89 and less than 93. You say me when you count by 10's. What number am I?

Name_____ Date_____

Count by 10's. Write the number.

1.

_____
- - - - - - - -
_____

2.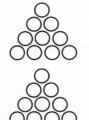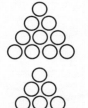

_____
- - - - - - - -
_____

3.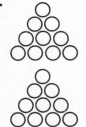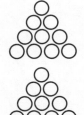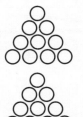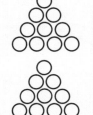

_____
- - - - - - - -
_____

Unit 5

4.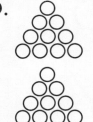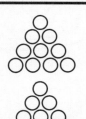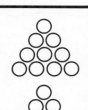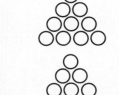

_____
- - - - - - - -
_____

5.

_____
- - - - - - - -
_____

Skip Counting: By 5's

Name_____ Date_____

Count by 5's. Write the missing numbers.

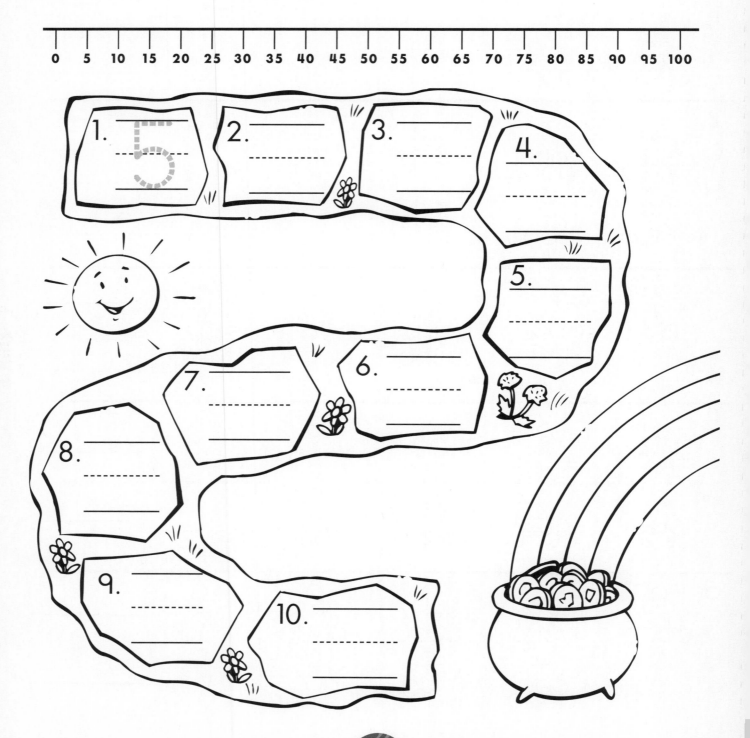

0 5 10 15 20 25 30 35 40 45 50 55 60 65 70 75 80 85 90 95 100

1. 5

2. ____

3. ____

4. ____

5. ____

6. ____

7. ____

8. ____

9. ____

10. ____

Skip Counting: By 2's

Name_____ Date_____

Count by 2's. Write the number.

1.

_____
- - - - - - - - - - -
_____

2.

_____
- - - - - - - - - - -
_____

3.

_____
- - - - - - - - - - -
_____

4.

_____
- - - - - - - - - - -
_____

5.

_____
- - - - - - - - - - -
_____

Unit 5

Skip Counting Practice

Name_____ Date_____

Count by 2's. Write the missing numbers.

1.  **2**  **4** 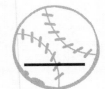 **6**  ___  ___

2.  ___  ___  ___  ___  **20**

Count by 5's. Write the missing numbers.

3.  **5**  **10**  ___  ___  ___

4.  ___  ___  **40**  ___  **50**

Count by 10's. Write the missing numbers.

5.  **10**  **20** ___ ___ ___

6.  ___  **70**  ___  ___ 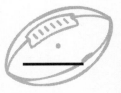 ___

Number Patterns (1)

Name_____ Date_____

Find the pattern. Write the missing numbers.

1.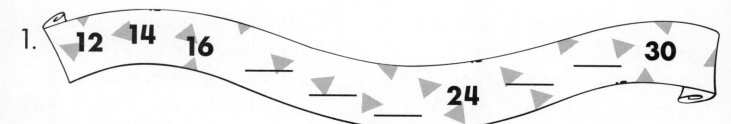
12 14 16 ___ ___ 24 ___ ___ 30

2.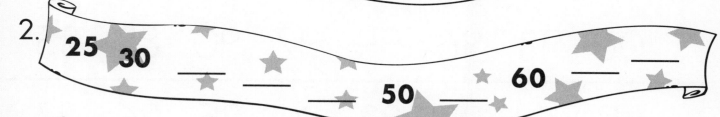
25 30 ___ ___ 50 ___ 60 ___ ___

3.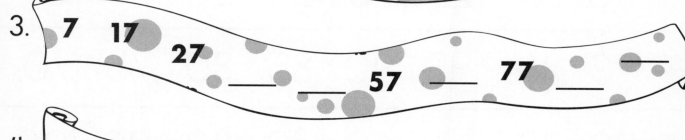
7 17 27 ___ ___ 57 ___ 77 ___

4.
48 46 44 ___ ___ 38 ___ 32 ___

5.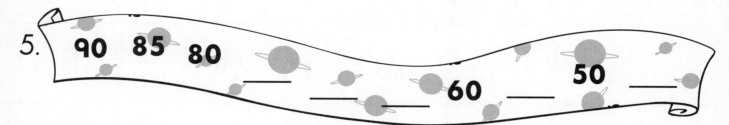
90 85 80 ___ ___ ___ 60 ___ 50 ___

6.
100 90 ___ ___ 60 ___ ___ 30 ___ ___

Unit 5

Number Patterns (II)

Name_____ Date_____

Look for the number patterns. Circle them.

Count by 1's from 57 to 62.   Count by 1's from 22 to 27.
Count by 2's from 2 to 12.   Count by 5's from 70 to 95.
Count by 2's from 88 to 100.   Count by 10's from 10 to 50.
Count by 5's from 15 to 45.   Count by 10's from 60 to 100.

100	98	96	94	92	90	88	85
45	0	22	23	24	25	26	27
23	14	95	90	85	80	75	70
30	19	12	60	70	80	90	100
25	57	58	59	60	61	62	80
30	10	20	30	40	50	43	85
15	20	25	30	35	40	45	67
10	91	2	4	6	8	10	12

Name_____ Date_____

Draw lines to match the pennies with the amounts.

1¢

2¢

3¢

4¢

Unit 5

5¢

6¢

7¢

9¢

Name_____ Date_____

A NICKEL IS WORTH 5¢.

Count by 5's. Write the amount.

1.

15
_____ ¢

2.

_____ ¢

3.

_____ ¢

4.

_____ ¢

5.

_____ ¢

6.

_____ ¢

Money: Dimes and Pennies

Name_____ Date_____

Count the money in each treasure chest. Write the amount.

1.

¢
_____

2.

¢
_____

3.

¢
_____

4.

¢
_____

5.

¢
_____

6.

¢
_____

Money Word Problems

Name_____ Date_____

Read each story problem. Write the answer.

1. Rebecca has two pennies in one hand.
   She has three dimes in the other hand.
   How much money does she have in all?

   ¢
   _____

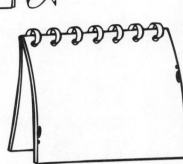

2. Kyle has one nickel.
   He finds two more nickels.
   How much money does he have in all?

   ¢
   _____

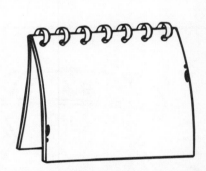

3. Todd has one nickel.
   Bob has nine pennies.
   How much money do they have altogether?

   ¢
   _____

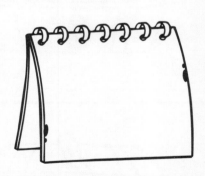

4. Jill has three dimes.
   Paul has five pennies.
   Who has more money?

   ¢
   _____

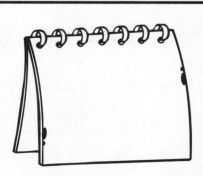

Money Practice (I)

Name_____ Date_____

Count the money. Write the amount.

1.

¢
_____

2.

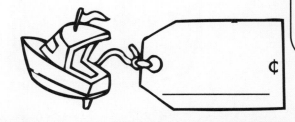
¢
_____

3.

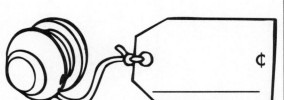
¢
_____

4.

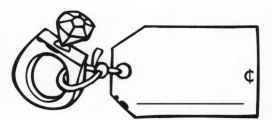
¢
_____

5.
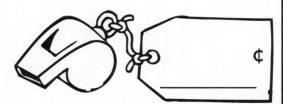
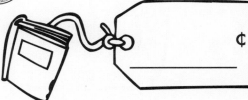
¢
_____

6.

¢
_____

Unit 5

Name_____ Date_____

Count the money in each jar. Circle the correct answer.

1.

20¢   30¢

2.

19¢   29¢

3.

92¢   96¢

4.

58¢   85¢

5.

18¢   34¢

6.

33¢   37¢

Name_____ Date_____

Count the money. Write the amount.

1.
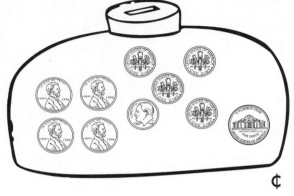
¢
_____

2.

¢
_____

3.

¢
_____

4.
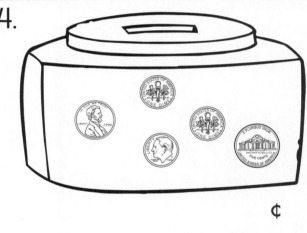
¢
_____

Unit 5

Read the problem. Circle the answer.

5. Bill has 2 dimes, 2 nickels, and 5 pennies. How much money does he have?

35¢   45¢

6. Kyra has one nickel and two dimes. Lynn as three nickels and eight pennies. Who has more money?

Kyra   Lynn

Name_____ Date_____

○ 31¢
● 36¢
○ 39¢

Count the money. Then fill in the circle next to the correct answer.

1.
○ 20¢
○ 25¢
○ 29¢

2.
○ 32¢
○ 36¢
○ 52¢

3.
○ 46¢
○ 56¢
○ 58¢

4.
○ 35¢
○ 50¢
○ 75¢

5.
○ 80¢
○ 85¢
○ 90¢

6.
○ 75¢
○ 77¢
○ 79¢

7.
○ 28¢
○ 38¢
○ 39¢

8.
○ 89¢
○ 95¢
○ 99¢

Name_____ Date_____

The **minute hand** is on **12**.
The **hour hand** is on **3**.
It is **3:00** or **3 o'clock**.

Circle the correct time.

1.

(5:00)   7:00

12:00   1:00

11:00   12:00

2.

8:00   10:00

11:00   9:00

1:00   2:00

3.

6 o'clock
7 o'clock

3 o'clock
2 o'clock

6 o'clock
12 o'clock

Unit 6

Name_____ Date_____

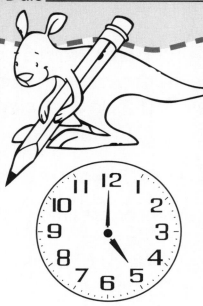

Draw a line from each clock to the matching time.

5 o'clock

3 o'clock

1 o'clock

6 o'clock

8 o'clock

2 o'clock

9 o'clock

4 o'clock

Time to the Hour (III)

Name_____ Date_____

Write the time.

1.

_____ o'clock   _____ o'clock   _____ o'clock

2.

_____ o'clock   _____ o'clock   _____ o'clock

3.

_____ o'clock   _____ o'clock   _____ o'clock

4.

_____ o'clock   _____ o'clock   _____ o'clock

Name_____ Date_____

Write the time.

1.

   9:00   _____ : _____   _____ : _____

2.

   _____ : _____   _____ : _____   _____ : _____

3.

   _____ : _____   _____ : _____   _____ : _____

4.

   _____ : _____   _____ : _____   _____ : _____

Time to the Hour (V)

Name_____ Date_____

Draw the hour hand on each clock to show the time.

1.

3:00   12:00   6:00

2.

7:00   2:00   5:00

3.

11:00   8:00   1:00

4.

4:00   9:00   10:00

Unit 6

Time to the Half Hour (I)

Minute hand on the 6.

Hour hand between 8 and 9.

8:30 or **eight-thirty**

Circle the correct time.

1.

8:30   9:30

1:30   11:30

12:30   1:30

2.

7:30   8:30

5:30   6:30

2:30   3:30

3.

three-thirty

two-thirty

nine-thirty

eight-thirty

four-thirty

five-thirty

Premium Education Math: Grade 1   120   © Learning Horizons

Name_____ Date_____

Draw a line from each clock to the matching time.

8:30

6:30

nine-thirty

7:30

5:30

12:30

4:30

one-thirty

Unit 6

Name_____ Date_____

Write the time.

1.

__one__-thirty

_____-thirty

_____-thirty

2.

_____-thirty

_____-thirty

_____-thirty

3.

_____-thirty

_____-thirty

_____-thirty

4.

_____-thirty

_____-thirty

_____-thirty

Name_____ Date_____

Write the time.

1.

10:30
_____

:
_____

:
_____

2.

:
_____

:
_____

:
_____

3.

:
_____

:
_____

:
_____

4.

:
_____

:
_____

:
_____

Unit 6

Name_____ Date_____

Draw the hour hand on each clock to show the time.

1.

6:30   8:30   7:30

2.

11:30   1:30   3:30

3.
 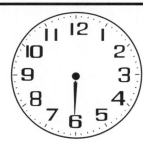 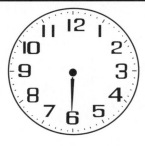

9:30   10:30   12:30

4.
  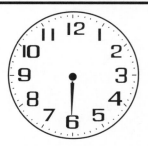

5:30   2:30   4:30

Elapsed Time

Now it is **2 o'clock**.   One hour later it will be **3 o'clock**.

Draw clock hands to show the time one hour later. Write the time.

NOW   **LATER**

1.    12 o'clock   ____ o'clock

2.    4 o'clock   ____ o'clock

3.    7 o'clock   ____ o'clock

4.    10 o'clock   ____ o'clock

Unit 6

Time Word Problems

Read each problem. Write the answer.

1. Eric left home at 11 o'clock. It took 1 hour to get to the beach. What time did Eric get to the beach?

_____

2. Kate goes to camp at 8 o'clock. Pat goes to camp at 9 o'clock. Who goes to camp first?

_____

3. Samir got to the park at 3 o'clock. He went home at 5 o'clock. For how long was Samir at the park?

_____

4. The soccer game starts at 6 o'clock. It ends one hour later. What time does the soccer game end?

_____

5. Meg left home at 9 o'clock. It took her 2 hours to get to Aunt Lin's. What time did Meg get to Aunt Lin's?

_____

6. Ben went to the pool at 2:00. He stayed for 1 hour. What time did Ben go home?

_____

Name_____ Date_____

Write the time.

1.
      (clock)

___:___   ___:___   ___:___

2.
(clock)   (clock)   (clock)

___:___   ___:___   ___:___

3.
   (clock)   (clock)

___:___   ___:___   ___:___

4.
   (clock)

___:___   ___:___   ___:___

Time Practice (II)

Name_____ Date_____

Circle the time.

| ten-thirty | 4 o'clock | 6:00 |
| eleven-thirty | 2 o'clock | 12:00 |

Draw lines to match the clocks with the same time.

Time Practice (III)

Name_____ Date_____

- ○ 7:00
- ● 8:00
- ○ 9:00

Fill in the circle next to the correct time.

1.
- ○ 7:30
- ○ 8:30
- ○ 9:30

2.
- ○ 7:00
- ○ 8:00
- ○ 9:00

3.
- ○ 2:00
- ○ 3:00
- ○ 3:30

4.
- ○ 4:30
- ○ 5:00
- ○ 5:30

5.
- ○ 11:30
- ○ 12:30
- ○ 1:30

6.
- ○ 5:00
- ○ 6:00
- ○ 12:30

7.
- ○ 1:00
- ○ 9:00
- ○ 10:00

8.
- ○ 1:30
- ○ 2:30
- ○ 3:30

Unit 6

Name_____ Date_____

Use the calendar to answer the questions.

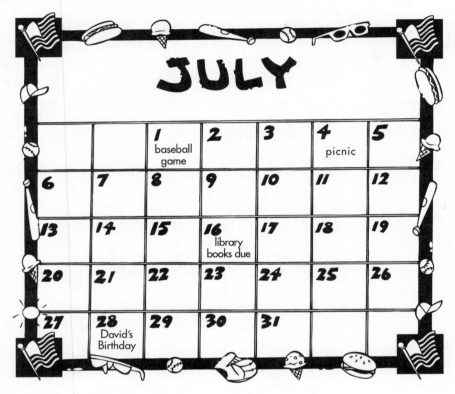

		1 baseball game	2	3	4 picnic	5
6	7	8	9	10	11	12
13	14	15	16 library books due	17	18	19
20	21	22	23	24	25	26
27	28 David's Birthday	29	30	31		

JULY

1. What is the first day of the week? _____

2. How many days are in one week? _____

3. How many Mondays are in this month? _____

4. What day of the week is July 10? _____

5. What is the date of the picnic? _____

6. When is David's birthday? _____

7. When are the library books due? _____

8. When is the baseball game? _____

Months of the Year

Read each clue. Write the answer.

| January | February | March | April | May | June | July |
| August | September | October | November | December |

1. First month of the year   January

2. Last month of the year   _____

3. Month after June   _____

4. Month before September   _____

5. Month between May and July   _____

6. Second month of the year   _____

7. Tenth month of the year   _____

8. Third month of the year   _____

9. Month between March and May   _____

10. Fifth month of the year   _____

11. Month before October   _____

12. Month before December   _____

Unit 6

Name_____ Date_____

Write the number of inches.

1.
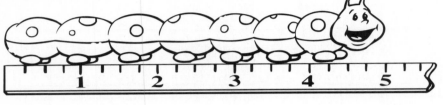

_____ inch(es) long

2.
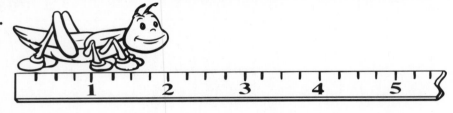

_____ inch(es) long

3.
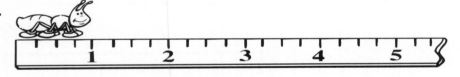

_____ inch(es) long

4.
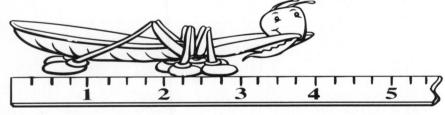

_____ inch(es) long

5.

_____ inch(es) long

Name_____ Date_____

Write the number of inches.

1.

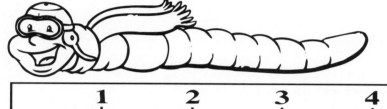

| 1 | 2 | 3 | 4 | 5 | 6 |

about _____ inch(es)

2.

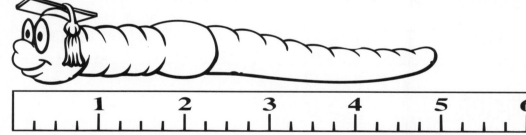

| 1 | 2 | 3 | 4 | 5 | 6 |

about _____ inch(es)

3.

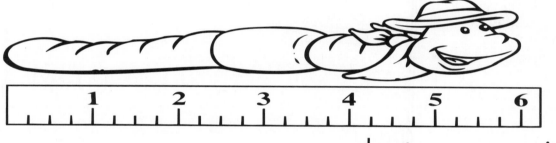

| 1 | 2 | 3 | 4 | 5 | 6 |

about _____ inch(es)

4.

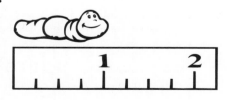

| 1 | 2 |

about _____ inch(es)

5.

| 1 | 2 | 3 |

about _____ inch(es)

Unit 6

Name_____ Date_____

Use an inch ruler to measure each path on the map.
Write the number of inches.

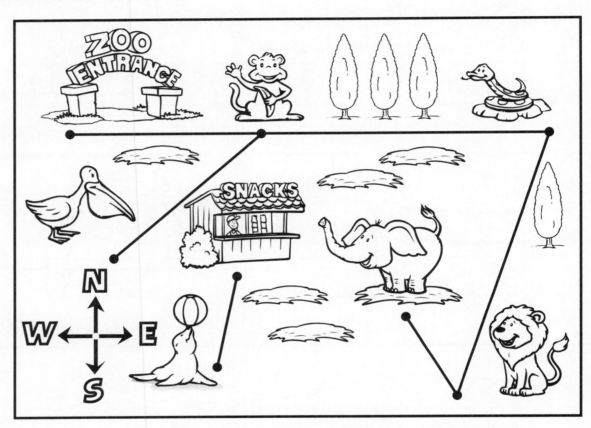

How long is the path:

1. From the Entrance to the Monkeys? _____ inch(es)

2. From the Entrance to the Snakes? _____ inch(es)

3. From the Monkeys to the Birds? _____ inch(es)

4. From the Snack Bar to the Seals? _____ inch(es)

5. From the Elephants to the Lions? _____ inch(es)

6. From the Lions to the Snakes? _____ inch(es)

Name_____ Date_____

Write the number of centimeters.

1.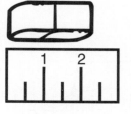

about _____ centimeters

2.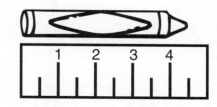

about _____ centimeters

3.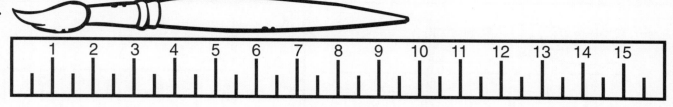

about _____ centimeters

4.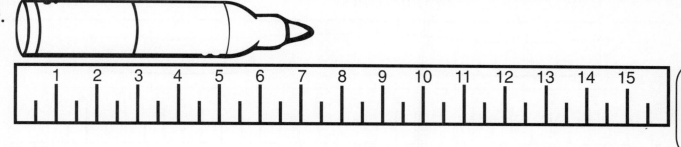

about _____ centimeters

Unit 6

5.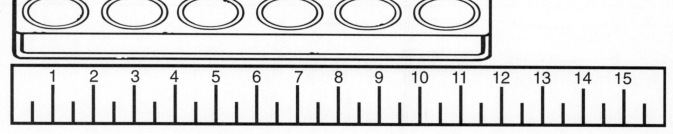

about _____ centimeters

Name_____ Date_____

Write the number of centimeters.

1.
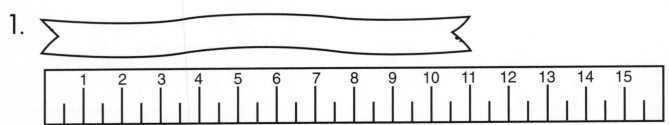

_____ centimeters

2.
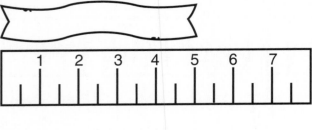

_____ centimeters

3.
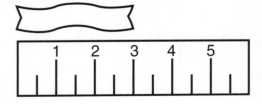

_____ centimeters

4.
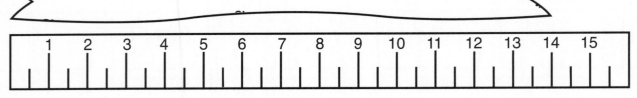

_____ centimeters

5.
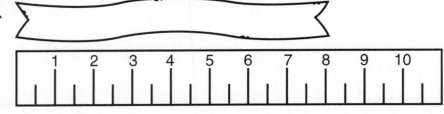

_____ centimeters

Name_____ Date_____

Write the number of centimeters.

1.
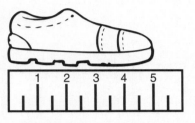

_____ centimeters

2.
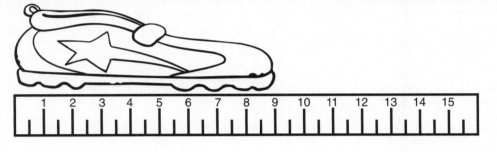

_____ centimeters

3.
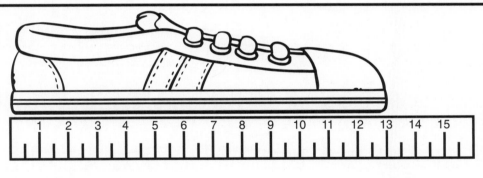

_____ centimeters

Unit 6

4.
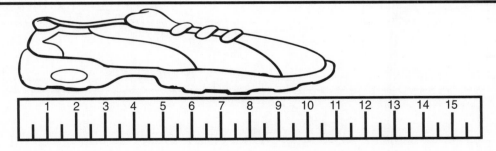

_____ centimeters

Name_____ Date_____

Estimate the length of each fish.
Then use a ruler to measure the number of inches or centimeters.

1.

Estimate: _____ centimeters   Measure: _____ centimeters

2.

Estimate: _____ inches   Measure: _____ inches

3.

Estimate: _____ centimeters   Measure: _____ centimeters

4.

Estimate: _____ inches   Measure: _____ inches

5.

Estimate:_____ centimeters   Measure:_____ centimeters

Practice Test: Facts to 10

Name_____ Date_____

Fill in the circle next to the correct answer.

1. ▲▲▲ ▲▲	○ 5 ○ 6 ○ 7	

1.		○ 5 ○ 6 ○ 7
2.	 + ■■	○ 5 ○ 6 ○ 7
3.	◆ ◆ ✕	○ 2 ○ 3 ○ 4
4.	7 + 3	○ 9 ○ 10 ○ 8
5.	9 – 5	○ 2 ○ 4 ○ 10
6.	5 – 4	○ 9 ○ 5 ○ 1
7.	6 + 1	○ 5 ○ 6 ○ 7
8.	10 – 8	○ 2 ○ 3 ○ 4
9.	7 – 3	○ 3 ○ 4 ○ 5
10.	4 + 4	○ 8 ○ 9 ○ 10
11.	8 – 8	○ 8 ○ 1 ○ 0
12.	3 + 0	○ 0 ○ 2 ○ 3

Unit 7

Name_____ Date_____

Fill in the circle next to the correct answer.

1. ★★★★★★ ★★★★★★	○ 12 ○ 13 ○ 14	2. ♥♥♥♥♥♥ + ♥♥♥♥♥	○ 9 ○ 10 ○ 11
3. ▮▮▮▮▮▮▮▮▮ ▮XXXXX	○ 8 ○ 9 ○ 15	4. 9 + 2	○ 9 ○ 10 ○ 11
5. 12 − 5	○ 7 ○ 8 ○ 9	6. 15 − 7	○ 7 ○ 8 ○ 9
7. 8 + 4	○ 10 ○ 11 ○ 12	8. 17 − 8	○ 8 ○ 9 ○ 10
9. 5 2 + 2	○ 7 ○ 9 ○ 11	10. 8 1 + 5	○ 14 ○ 15 ○ 16
11. 13 − 5	○ 4 ○ 6 ○ 8	12. 9 +18	○ 9 ○ 8 ○ 7

Practice Test: Word Problems

Name_____ Date_____

Fill in the circle next to the correct answer.

1. Jill had 9 pencils.
   She gave 4 away.
   How many pencils does she have left?

   ○ 5
   ○ 4
   ○ 13

2. Paul had 7 fish.
   He bought 4 more.
   How many fish does he have in all?

   ○ 2
   ○ 3
   ○ 11

3. Terry had 8 donuts.
   She gave 5 away.
   How many donuts does she have left?

   ○ 2
   ○ 3
   ○ 14

4. Sara read 3 books.
   Jackie read 8 books.
   How many books were read in all?

   ○ 5
   ○ 10
   ○ 11

5. Eric has 7 hats.
   Joe had 8 hats.
   How many hats are there in all?

   ○ 14
   ○ 15
   ○ 16

6. Michelle had 6 cookies.
   She ate 4 of them.
   How many cookies does she have left?

   ○ 2
   ○ 3
   ○ 10

Unit 7

Practice Test: Shapes and Fractions

Name_____ Date_____

Fill in the circle next to the correct answer.

1. ○ square ○ triangle ○ circle	2. ○ cylinder ○ cube ○ square
3. ○ square ○ rectangle ○ triangle	4. ○ cylinder ○ circle ○ square
5. ○ congruent ○ not congruent ○ square	6. ○ congruent ○ not congruent ○ square
7. ○ square ○ rectangle ○ triangle	8. ○ triangle ○ rectangle ○ square
9. ○ $\frac{1}{4}$ ○ $\frac{1}{2}$ ○ $\frac{1}{3}$	10. ○ $\frac{1}{2}$ ○ $\frac{1}{3}$ ○ $\frac{1}{4}$
11. ○ $\frac{1}{2}$ ○ $\frac{1}{3}$ ○ $\frac{1}{4}$	12. ○ $\frac{1}{3}$ ○ $\frac{1}{4}$ ○ $\frac{1}{2}$

Practice Test: Graphs

Name_____ Date_____

Fill in the circle next to the correct answer.

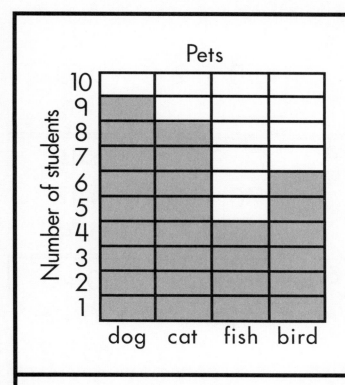

Pets

Number of students: 10 9 8 7 6 5 4 3 2 1

dog   cat   fish   bird

1. How many students have dogs?
   ○ 8
   ○ 9
   ○ 10

2. How many students have fish?
   ○ 4
   ○ 6
   ○ 8

3. How many students have cats?
   ○ 6
   ○ 7
   ○ 8

4. How many children have birthdays in March?
   ○ 1
   ○ 2
   ○ 3

5. How many children have birthdays in August?
   ○ 3
   ○ 4
   ○ 6

6. How many children have birthdays in July?
   ○ 0
   ○ 1
   ○ 2

Birthdays

March	🎂 🎂
June	🎂 🎂
July	🎂
August	🎂 🎂 🎂

🎂 = 1 child

Unit 7

Practice Test: Place Value

Name_____ Date_____

Fill in the circle next to the correct answer.

1. $40 + 7$	○ 40 ○ 47 ○ 74	**2.** $50 + 2$	○ 25 ○ 50 ○ 52
3. $10 + 8$	○ 18 ○ 20 ○ 24	**4.** $70 + 4$	○ 44 ○ 47 ○ 74
5. 35	○ $30 + 5$ ○ $40 + 5$ ○ $50 + 3$	**6.** 26	○ $10 + 6$ ○ $20 + 6$ ○ $60 + 2$
7. 69	○ $90 + 6$ ○ $70 + 0$ ○ $60 + 9$	**8.** 91	○ $10 + 9$ ○ $90 + 1$ ○ $90 + 9$
9. 2 tens 5 ones	○ 22 ○ 25 ○ 52	**10.** 8 tens 2 ones	○ 82 ○ 88 ○ 89
11. 6 tens 8 ones	○ 86 ○ 78 ○ 68	**12.** 1 ten 3 ones	○ 10 ○ 13 ○ 31

Name_____ Date_____

Fill in the circle next to the correct answer.

1.		
	40 + 10	○ 30 ○ 40 ○ 50

2.		
	52 + 23	○ 31 ○ 77 ○ 87

3.		
	66 − 21	○ 45 ○ 47 ○ 56

4.		
	36 + 51	○ 85 ○ 86 ○ 87

5.		
	98 − 88	○ 10 ○ 18 ○ 20

6.		
	81 − 20	○ 60 ○ 61 ○ 71

7.		
	76 − 44	○ 23 ○ 32 ○ 41

8.		
	12 + 87	○ 99 ○ 89 ○ 86

9. Melanie had 89 marbles.
   She gave 45 away.
   How many marbles does she have left?
   ○ 44 ○ 45 ○ 54

10. Frank had 52 baseball cards.
    His dad gave him 12 more.
    How many baseball cards does he have in all?
    ○ 44 ○ 60 ○ 64

Unit 7

Practice Test: Number Order

Name_____ Date_____

Fill in the circle next to the correct answer.

1. What comes before 76?
- ○ 75
- ○ 77
- ○ 80

2. What comes between 41 and 43?
- ○ 38
- ○ 40
- ○ 42

3. What comes after 59?
- ○ 60
- ○ 58
- ○ 55

4. What comes before 50?
- ○ 56
- ○ 51
- ○ 49

5. What comes after 69?
- ○ 59
- ○ 68
- ○ 70

6. one, two, ____
- ○ four
- ○ three
- ○ two

7. five, ____, seven
- ○ six
- ○ eight
- ○ nine

8. 23 ☐ 32
- ○ >
- ○ <
- ○ =

9. 60 ☐ 59
- ○ >
- ○ <
- ○ =

10. 89 ☐ 86
- ○ >
- ○ <
- ○ =

11. ↓ ☐ ☐ ☐ ☐
- ○ first
- ○ second
- ○ third

12. ↓ ☐ ☐ ☐ ☐
- ○ first
- ○ second
- ○ third

Name_____ Date_____

Fill in the circle next to the correct answer.

1. 5, 10, 15, ___ ○ 25 ○ 15 ○ 20	**2.** 10, 20, 30, ___ ○ 30 ○ 40 ○ 50
3. 2, 4, 6, ___ ○ 8 ○ 7 ○ 6	**4.** 40, 50, 60, ___ ○ 65 ○ 70 ○ 75
5. 14, 16, 18, ___ ○ 18 ○ 20 ○ 24	**6.** 30, 35, 40, ___ ○ 45 ○ 50 ○ 55
7. 44, 45, 46, ___ ○ 47 ○ 48 ○ 49	**8.** 22, 24, 26, ___ ○ 27 ○ 28 ○ 29
9. 70, 80, 90, ___ ○ 60 ○ 95 ○ 100	**10.** 57, 58, 59, ___ ○ 50 ○ 60 ○ 70
11. 15, 20, 25, ___ ○ 30 ○ 35 ○ 40	**12.** 40, 42, 44, ___ ○ 43 ○ 45 ○ 46

Unit 7

Name_____ Date_____

Fill in the circle next to the correct answer.

1. 
○ 1¢
○ 5¢
○ 10¢

2. 
○ 1¢
○ 5¢
○ 10¢

3. 
○ 1¢
○ 5¢
○ 10¢

4. 
○ 5¢
○ 6¢
○ 7¢

5. 
○ 10¢
○ 15¢
○ 20¢

6. 
○ 60¢
○ 50¢
○ 40¢

7. 
○ 6¢
○ 27¢
○ 28¢

8. 
○ 12¢
○ 17¢
○ 20¢

9. Karen has 35¢. The candy bar she wants to buy is 75¢. How much more money does Karen need?
○ 30¢
○ 35¢
○ 40¢

10. Warren has 50¢.
Bob has 45¢.
How much money do they have altogether?
○ 85¢
○ 95¢
○ 99¢

Name_____ Date_____

Fill in the circle next to the correct answer.

1.		2.	
	○ 3:00 ○ 4:00 ○ 5:00		○ 3:00 ○ 6:00 ○ 9:00

3.		4.	
	○ 12:30 ○ 1:30 ○ 2:30		○ 9:30 ○ 10:30 ○ 11:30

5.		6.	
	○ 12:00 ○ 1:00 ○ 2:00		○ 4:30 ○ 5:30 ○ 6:30

7.		8.	
6 o'clock	○ 12:00 ○ 1:00 ○ 6:00	eight-thirty	○ 8:00 ○ 8:30 ○ 9:30

9.

It is now 2 o'clock. In two hours it will be ____.

○ 3:00
○ 3:30
○ 4:00

10.

Jill has soccer practice at 5:00. If the practice lasts 1 hour, what time will it be over?

○ 5:30
○ 6:00
○ 7:00

Unit 7

Name_____ Date_____

Fill in the circle next to the correct answer.

September

Sun	Mon	Tue	Wed	Thur	Fri	Sat
	1	2	3	4	5	6
7	8	9	10	11	12	13
14	15	16	17	18	19	20
21	22	23	24	25	26	27
28	29	30				

1. How many Tuesdays are in September?
   ○ 3
   ○ 4
   ○ 5

2. How many days are in September?
   ○ 28
   ○ 29
   ○ 30

3. How many months are in one year?
   ○ 10
   ○ 11
   ○ 12

4. What is the first month of the year?
   ○ January
   ○ February
   ○ July

5. How long is this string?
   ○ 3 inches
   ○ 4 inches
   ○ 5 inches

6. How long is this string?
   ○ 8 centimeters
   ○ 9 centimeters
   ○ 10 centimeters

Page 3

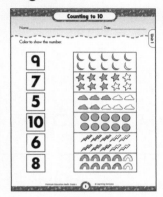

Page 4
1. 6   2. 5
3. 7   4. 9
5. 4   6. 8   7. 10

Page 5
1. 10   2. 8
3. 10   4. 7
5. 6   6. 9

Page 6
1. $3 + 6 = 9$
2. $5 + 4 = 9$
3. $8 + 2 = 10$
4. $6 + 2 = 8$
5. $0 + 7 = 7$
6. $3 + 5 = 8$

Page 7
1. 10, 9, 4, 9
2. 9, 7, 9, 3
3. 10, 8, 7, 5

Page 8

Page 9
1. 10, 6   5. 3, 10
2. 9, 9   6. 7, 5
3. 5, 3   7. 10, 6
4. 9, 8

Page 10
1. 10, 6, 8, 10, 7
2. 9, 3, 9, 7, 5
3. 10, 5, 8, 4, 8
4. 10, 8, 6, 9, 5

Page 11

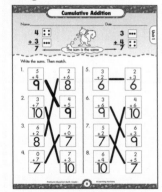

Page 12
1. 5   4. 2
2. 4   5. 6
3. 4

Page 13
1. 5
2. 1   3. 4
4. 3   5. 3
6. 5   7. 3

Page 14
1. $10 - 3 = 7$
2. $10 - 8 = 2$
3. $9 - 6 = 3$
4. $10 - 5 = 5$
5. $8 - 4 = 4$

Page 15
1. 3
2. 5   3. 2
4. 4   5. 6
6. 1

Page 16
1. 4, 3, 3, 5
2. 0, 4, 8, 1
3. 4, 2, 4, 2

Page 17
1. 3, 3, 0, 3
2. 5, 3, 5, 1
3. 3, 2, 3, 4

Page 18
1. 3, 2, 4, 4, 2
2. 0, 2, 2, 3, 7
3. 0, 0, 2, 3, 3
4. 8, 1, 2, 2, 1

Answer Key

Page 19
1. 2, 5   4. 7, 10
2. 4, 9   5. 3, 9
3. 2, 6

Page 20
1. 4   2. 2
3. 1   4. 4
5. 4   6. 9
7. 9   8. 5

Page 21
1. 3   2. 9
3. 8   4. 1
5. 4   6. 3
7. 10   8. 0

Page 22
1. 9   3. 7
2. 8   4. 4

Page 23
1. 6   4. 8
2. 5   5. 4
3. 9

Page 24
1. 1   4. 2
2. 3   5. 5
3. 5

Page 25
1. 2   4. 3
2. 1   5. 4
3. 6

Page 26
1. 7   4. 9
2. 4   5. 4
3. 6

Page 27

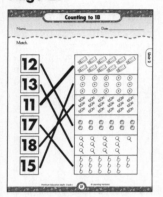

Page 28
1. 18   4. 16
2. 17   5. 13
3. 16

Page 29
1. 17
2. 15   3. 17
4. 16   5. 15
6. 13   7. 14

Page 30
1. 18
2. 17, 16
3. 11, 12, 13
4. 12, 14, 15
5. 16, 11, 12
6. 14, 11, 12

Page 31
1. 17, 11, 18, 14, 12
2. 15, 13, 14, 16, 12
3. 11, 13, 11, 12, 14

Page 32

Page 33
1. 8, 3, 5, 8
2. 8, 9, 9, 4
3. 8, 6, 10, 7

Page 34
1. 14, 14, 15, 12, 12
2. 17, 16, 10, 11, 13

Page 35
1. 9, 10, 13, 9, 12
2. 13, 14, 12, 11, 9
3. 12, 11, 13, 12, 13

Page 36
1. 7   4. 9
2. 5   5. 8
3. 3

Page 37
1. 8
2. 8   3. 9
4. 6   5. 9
6. 9   7. 5

Page 38
1. 9, 5, 8, 8
2. 6, 6, 8, 9
3. 9, 3, 7, 7

Page 39

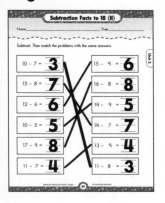

Page 40

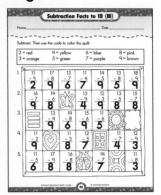

Page 41
1. 8, 3, 12, 3
2. 16, 9, 7, 12
3. 9, 11, 5, 4
4. 9, 2, 7, 11

Page 42
1. 4, 4   4. 8, 8
2. 7, 7   5. 6, 6
3. 9, 9   6. 9, 9

Page 43
1. 13, ⑥, 9, ⑪
2. ⑨, ⑪ 7, 8
3. 14, ⑱ 7, ⑨
4. 7, ⑦ 11, 15

Page 44
1. 6   2. 11
3. 11   4. 3
5. 7   6. 14
7. 11   8. 8

Page 45
1. 11   3. 15
2. 15   4. 11

Page 46
1. 13   3. 13
2. 11   4. 17

Page 47
1. 6   3. 7
2. 9   4. 8

Page 48
1. 9   3. 8
2. 9   4. 6

Page 49
1. 13 – 6 = 7
2. 9 + 7 = 16
3. 15 – 8 = 7
4. 12 – 5 = 7
5. 5 + 9 = 14
6. 3 + 9 = 12

page 50

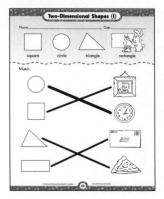

Page 51

Page 52

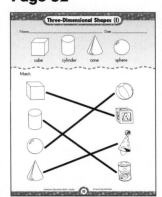

Answer Key

page 53

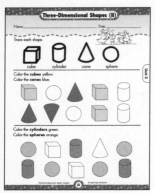

Page 54

1. apple
   pear
   strawberry
   banana
2. trumpet
   drum
   tambourine
   bell
3. circle
   square
   heart
   triangle
4. seahorse
   snail
   starfish
   crab

Page 55

1. peanut
   walnut
   almond
   buckeye
2. car
   airplane
   bus
   boat
3. penny
   nickel
   dime
   quarter
4. shoes
   shorts
   shirt
   socks

Page 56

1. ○   4. △

2. □   5. △

3. △   6. □

Page 57

1. ○   4. □

2. □   5. □

3. □   6. ◁

Page 58

1. △   △

2. □   ▭

3. ⬭   ⬭

4. □   □

Page 59

1. ○   2. ▭

3. △   4. ⌐┘

5. ⬛   6. △

Page 60

1. 9   3. 6
2. 7   4. 4

Page 61

Page 62

1. 3
2. 6
3. 7
4. 4

Page 63

1. 7
2. 3
3. 9
4. 8

Page 64

1. 5
2. 3
3. 4
4. 1

Answer Key

Page 65
1. 4   5. 5
2. 10   6. 3
3. 2   7. 1
4. 16   8. 4

page 66
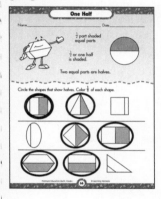

page 67
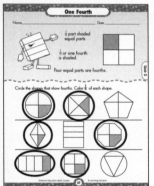

Page 68
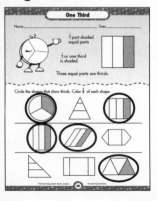

Page 69
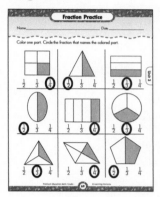

Page 70
1. 4 tens 7 ones = 47
2. 9 tens 2 ones = 92
3. 5 tens 2 ones = 52
4. 7 tens 0 ones = 70
5. 6 tens 8 ones = 68
6. 8 tens 5 ones = 85

Page 71
1. 35, 82, 71
2. 63, 47, 22
3. 19, 91, 56
4. 32, 85, 68
5. 40 + 9
   20 + 6
   10 + 5
6. 50 + 3
   40 + 5
   60 + 2
7. 70 + 4
   80 + 0
   70 + 9
8. 50 + 7
   60 + 1
   90 + 8

Page 72
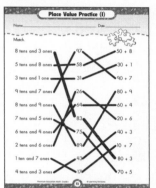

Page 73
1. 4 tens 5 ones = 45
2. 5 tens 3 ones = 53
3. 2 tens 7 ones = 27
4. 3 tens 5 ones, 5 tens 4 ones
5. 8 tens 1 one, 2 tens, 9 ones
6. 43, 16
7. 60, 99

Page 74
1. 50, 90
2. 60, 80, 70, 70, 90, 90
3. 80, 80, 90, 60, 50, 80

Page 75
1. 49, 44, 66, 86
2. 89, 58, 77, 65
3. 39, 55, 92, 93
4. 79, 78, 87, 98

Page 76
1. 69, 73, 54, 39
2. 98, 84, 75, 59
3. 69, 73, 54, 48
4. 39, 58, 47, 37

Page 77
1. 49, 88
2. 67, 83, 79, 48, 68
3. 99, 92, 97, 89, 96
4. 91, 75, 89, 85, 98

Page 78
1. 89, 88, 68, 74, 88
2. 89, 73, 98, 66, 65
3. 99, 33, 79, 89, 89
4. 97, 86, 99, 99, 88

Page 79
1. 31, 33
2. 11, 44, 58, 30, 12
3. 33, 23, 31, 12, 64

Page 80
1. 24, 35, 18, 14
2. 64, 31, 23, 31
3. 32, 42, 37, 42
4. 26, 11, 24, 57

Page 81
1. 41, 10, 21, 32, 41
2. 11, 32, 22, 22, 41
3. 33, 34, 81, 44, 11
4. 65, 28, 26, 20, 37

Page 82
1. 24   2. 46
3. 67   4. 64
5. 51   6. 21
7. 70   8. 23

Page 83
1. 40   2. 70
3. 32   4. 50
5. 58   6. 98
7. 25   8. 76

Page 84
1. 39   2. 23
3. 53   4. 79
5. 33   6. 78
7. 68   8. 86
9. 13   10. 69

Page 85
1. 32 + 57 = 89
2. 52 + 26 = 78
3. 87 + 12 = 99
4. 31 + 48 = 79
5. 24 + 51 = 75
6. 37 + 21 = 58

Page 86
1. 42 + 23 = 65
2. 31 + 31 = 62
3. 45 + 10 = 55
4. 10 + 34 = 44
5. 31 + 23 = 54
6. 54 + 31 = 85
7. 42 + 42 = 84
8. 45 + 34 = 79
9. Mai
10. Nick

Page 87
1. 49 – 38 = 11
2. 96 – 74 = 22
3. 67 – 42 = 25
4. 95 – 45 = 50
5. 56 – 14 = 42
6. 78 – 35 = 43
7. 82 – 20 = 62
8. 99 – 65 = 34

Page 88
1. 62 – 30 = 32
2. 62 – 41 = 21
3. 27 – 15 = 12
4. 89 – 47 = 42
5. 78 – 36 = 42
6. 38 – 15 = 23
7. 56 – 45 = 11
8. 99 – 85 = 14

Page 89
1. 85 – 42 = 43
2. 63 + 26 = 89
3. 24 + 13 = 37
4. 39 – 10 = 29
5. 55 + 32 = 87
6. 41 – 20 = 21
7. 84 – 13 = 71
8. 24 + 41 = 65

Page 90

Page 91
1. 17, 43, 25, 51
2. 27, 15, 67
3. 11, 9, 23, 91
4. 47, 5, 9, 13
5. 80, 52, 46, 90
6. 18, 66, 40, 82
7. 2, 50, 78
8. 64, 58, 70
9. 15
10. 14

Page 92
1. 36   2. 88
3. 16   4. 22
5. 49   6. 60
7. 97   8. 79

Page 93
1. 10, 13, 20
2. 24, 29, 31
3. 37, 41, 45
4. 50, 55, 62
5. 67, 71, 79
6. 88, 93, 100

Page 94
1. 27, 15
2. 52, 69
3. 84, 41
4. 33, 96
5. 75, 30

Page 95
1. 10, 20, 30
2. 57, 68, 75
3. 14, 18, 23
4. 27, 31, 35
5. 45, 48, 52
6. 53, 67, 82
7. 29, 34, 41
8. 47, 59, 60
9. 68, 77, 90

Page 96
1. >, <, <
2. >, >, <
3. <, <, >
4. <, <, <
5. >, <, <
6. >, <, <

Page 97
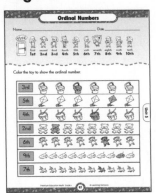

Page 98
1. 73, 74, 76, 77, 78, 80
2. 82, 83, 85, 86, 88, 89
3. 91, 92, 94, 95, 97, 99, 100
4. 54, 19, 37, 50
5. 30, 88, 13, 74
6. <, >, >, <
7. >, <, >, >
8. 45
9. 90

Page 99
1. 40   4. 80
2. 70   5. 100
3. 50

Page 100
1. 5   2. 10
3. 15   4. 20
5. 25   6. 30
7. 35   8. 40
9. 45   10. 50

Page 101
1. 6   2. 14
3. 8   4. 10
5. 18

Page 102
1. 8, 10
2. 12, 14, 16, 18
3. 15, 20, 25
4. 30, 35, 45
5. 30, 40, 50
6. 60, 80, 90, 100

Page 103
1. 18, 20, 22, 26, 28
2. 35, 40, 45, 55, 65, 70
3. 37, 47, 67, 87, 97
4. 42, 40, 36, 34, 30
5. 75, 70, 65, 55, 45
6. 80, 70, 50, 40, 20, 10

Page 104
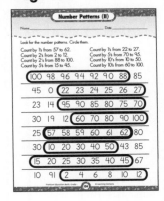

Page 105
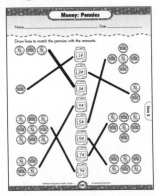

Page 106
1. 15¢
2. 25¢
3. 5¢
4. 20¢
5. 10¢
6. 30¢

Page 107
1. 7¢
2. 9¢
3. 15¢
4. 17¢
5. 15¢
6. 8¢

Page 108
1. 40¢
4. 80¢
2. 70¢
5. 50¢
3. 20¢
6. 30¢

Page 109
1. 22¢
2. 16¢
3. 60¢
4. 31¢
5. 13¢
6. 24¢

Page 110
1. 32¢
3. 14¢
2. 15¢
4. Jill

Page 111
1. 15¢
2. 40¢
3. 36¢
4. 44¢
5. 23¢
6. 47¢

Page 112
1. 20¢
2. 29¢
3. 96¢
4. 58¢
5. 18¢
6. 37¢

Page 113
1. 59¢
2. 73¢
3. 47¢
4. 36¢
5. 35¢
6. Kyra

Page 114
1. 29¢
2. 32¢
3. 56¢
4. 35¢
5. 85¢
6. 77¢
7. 38¢
8. 99¢

Page 115
1. 5:00, 1:00, 11:00
2. 10:00, 9:00, 2:00
3. 7 o'clock, 3 o'clock, 6 o'clock

Page 116
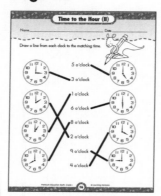

Page 117
1. 1, 3, 7
2. 9, 6, 2
3. 4, 12, 10
4. 8, 5, 11

Page 118
1. 9:00, 4:00, 7:00
2. 2:00, 11:00, 3:00
3. 5:00, 1:00, 6:00
4. 8:00. 12:00, 10:00

Page 119

Page 120
1. 9:30, 11:30. 12:30
2. 7:30, 5:30, 3:30
3. two-thirty, eight-thirty, four-thirty

Page 121
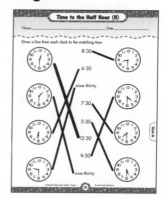

Page 122
1. 1:30, 9:30, 7:30
2. 2:30, 12:30, 4:30
3. 8:30, 3:30, 10:30
4. 5:30, 11:30, 6:30

Page 123
1. 10:30, 7:30, 4:30
2. 12:30, 1:30, 6:30
3. 5:30, 8:30, 2:30
4. 3:30, 11:30, 9:30

Page 124

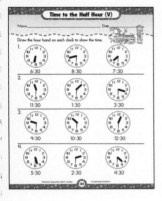

Page 125

1. 1:00

2. 5:00

3. 8:00

4. 11:00

Page 126
1. 12:00
2. Kate
3. 2 hours
4. 7 o'clock or 7:00
5. 11 o'clock or 11:00
6. 3:00

Page 127
1. 3:30, 9:00, 1:00
2. 5:00, 1:30, 7:30
3. 2:30, 11:00, 6:00
4. 8:30, 8:00, 12:30

Page 128

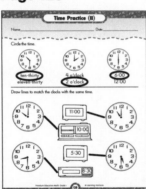

Page 129
1. 9:30
2. 7:00
3. 3:00
4. 4:30
5. 11:30
6. 6:00
7. 10:00
8. 2:30

Page 130
1. Sunday
2. 7
3. 4
4. Thursday
5. July 4
6. July 28
7. July 16
8. July 1

Page 131
1. January
2. December
3. July
4. August
5. June
6. February
7. October
8. March
9. April
10. May
11. September
12. November

Page 132
1. 5   4. 4
2. 2   5. 3
3. 1

Page 133
1. 4
2. 6
3. 5
4. 1   5. 2

Page 134
1. 2   4. 1
2. 5   5. 1
3. 2   6. 3

Answer Key

Page 135
1. 2
2. 4
3. 10
4. 7
5. 12

Page 136
1. 11
2. 5
3. 3
4. 14
5. 8

Page 137
1. 5
3. 13
2. 9
4. 11

Page 138
1. 8
4. 6
2. 4
5. 3
3. 5

Page 139
1. 5
2. 6
3. 2
4. 10
5. 4
6. 1
7. 7
8. 2
9. 4
10. 8
11. 0
12. 3

Page 140
1. 12
2. 11
3. 9
4. 11
5. 7
6. 8
7. 12
8. 9
9. 9
10. 14
11. 8
12. 9

Page 141
1. 5
4. 11
2. 11
5. 15
3. 3
6. 2

Page 142
1. circle
2. cube
3. rectangle
4. cylinder
5. congruent
6. not congruent
7. square
8. rectangle
9. $\frac{1}{3}$
10. $\frac{1}{4}$
11. $\frac{1}{2}$
12. $\frac{3}{4}$

Page 143
1. 9
4. 2
2. 4
5. 3
3. 8
6. 1

Page 144
1. 47
2. 52
3. 18
4. 74
5. 30 + 5
6. 20 + 6
7. 60 + 9
8. 90 + 1
9. 25
10. 82
11. 68
12. 13

Page 145
1. 50
2. 77
3. 45
4. 87
5. 10
6. 61
7. 32
8. 99
9. 44
10. 64

Page 146
1. 75
2. 42
3. 60
4. 49
5. 70
6. three
7. six
8. <
9. >
10. >
11. second
12. third

Page 147
1. 20
2. 40
3. 8
4. 70
5. 20
6. 45
7. 47
8. 28
9. 100
10. 60
11. 30
12. 46

Page 148
1. 5¢
2. 1¢
3. 10¢
4. 6¢
5. 20¢
6. 50¢
7. 28¢
8. 17¢
9. 40¢
10. 95¢

Page 149
1. 4:00
2. 9:00
3. 12:30
4. 10:30
5. 2:00
6. 4:30
7. 6:00
8. 8:30
9. 4:00
10. 6:00

Page 150
1. 5
2. 30
3. 12
4. January
5. 3 inches
6. 9 centimeters